CONDITIONING IN STUTTERING THERAPY:

APPLICATIONS AND LIMITATIONS

Stuttering

SPEECH FOUNDATION OF AMERICA
Publication No. 7

1

RC
424
.C6x

Speech Foundation of America
152 Lombardy Road
Memphis, Tennessee 38111

Additional copies of this booklet $1.00.

To The Reader

For many years it has been apparent that learning plays a very important role in creating and maintaining some, if not all, of the behaviors found in stuttering. While no agreement has been reached in this important matter, the recent emphasis upon conditioning procedures to modify or prevent stuttering has had a strong impact on the field of speech pathology.

To explore the subject and to put this information about conditioning into the hands of practicing therapists, this Foundation arranged for a conference of leading advocates of operant and classical conditioning therapy to meet with other eminent speech pathologists who had some pronounced reservations on the subject. We hoped to provide an objective, balanced point of view which would be of value to the clinician. This conference, lasting a week, was held in Montego Bay, Jamaica, and was concluded this year.

Each participant, whose name is listed on the following two pages, was asked to prepare a paper on some phase of the subject and to be prepared to discuss all the contributions critically. The material in this book is the result of these discussions and presentations. Although the participants were unable to reach agreement, we feel that by making available these revised papers along with a summary of the discussion by the Chairman, we offer the practicing therapist a better understanding of behavior modification through conditioning procedures.

The Foundation is dedicated to the cause of improving treatment of the stutterer and this is our latest contribution. Earlier publications are listed on the last page of this book.

MALCOLM FRASER

For the Speech Foundation of America
Memphis, Tennessee
July 1, 1970

76854

3

Participants

Stanley Ainsworth, Ph.D., Chairman
Associate dean for Research and Graduate Studies and distinguished professor of Speech Correction, University of Georgia. President (1960) and executive vice-president (1955-59) American Speech and Hearing Association.

Richard M. Boehmler, Ph.D.
Professor of speech pathology and audiology. Coordinator of Speech and Hearing Clinics, University of Montana. Consultant, speech and hearing programs, Montana State Department of Public Instruction.

Gene J. Brutten, Ph.D.
Professor, Departments of Speech Pathology and Psychology, Southern Illinois University Fellow, American Speech and Hearing Association. Co-author "The Modification of Stuttering" and other publications.

P. Helbert Damsté, M. D., Ph.D.
Lector in Foniatrie, University of Utrecht, President of the Nederlandse Vereniging voor Fonetische Weterschappen. Vice-President of the International Association of Logopedics and Phoniatrics. Editor of Folia Phoniatrica.

Albert T. Murphy, Ph.D.
Professor and chairman, Department of Special Education, Schools of Education and Medicine, Boston University. Author "Stuttering and Personality Dynamics" and other books.

Participants

Bruce P. Ryan, Ph.D.
Research associate, Monterey Institute for Speech and Hearing. Associate professor, Speech Department, University of Oregon.

George H. Shames, Ph.D.
Professor of speech and psychology. Director of the Graduate Training Program in Speech Pathology/Audiology, University of Pittsburgh.

Joseph G. Sheehan, Ph.D.
Professor of psychology, University of California, Los Angeles. Associate editor, Journal of Speech and Hearing Disorders (1958-65), and Asha (1964-68). Editor, "Stuttering: Research and Therapy."

C. Woodruff Starkweather, Ph.D., Editor
Assistant professor, Communication Sciences, Hunter College, Head, Publications Department, and editorial manager, "Journal of Speech and Hearing Disorders" (1965-1966), American Speech and Hearing Association.

Charles Van Riper, Ph.D.
Psychologist and speech pathologist, distinguished professor, Western Michigan University. Councilor (1950-53), honors of the American Speech and Hearing Association. Author "Speech Correction, Principles and Methods" and other books.

Malcolm Fraser
Director, Speech Foundation of America.

Table of Contents

PART I

PART II

PART III

PART IV

7

Behavior Modification: An Overview

CHARLES VAN RIPER, Ph.D.

Since its early beginnings, our profession has been built on a foundation of learning theory, and modern behavior modification constitutes only the latest storey of the edifice. In the 1930's we called ourselves the American Speech Correction Association and thought of ourselves as speech correctionists rather than as healers in the medical sense. Unlike the occupational and physical therapists we identified ourselves and our training centers not with the medical profession but with the schools and colleges and universities. Even today most of our workers find jobs in these settings. Our affiliation has always been closer to education than to medicine, to psychology than to psychiatry. We have always dealt with problems of learning and unlearning. Our basic function has been to modify communicative behaviors so that the people who came to us would be able to communicate more effectively.

It is not surprising, then, to find that we are now showing a lively interest in modern behavior theory and therapy. We have always hungered for better ways to help our clients. Unlike some other professions, we have a history of greeting new theories and technologies with enthusiasm rather than resistance—perhaps because we know how young we are as a profession. We know we are all still pioneers.

Being inveterate explorers, we are also pragmatists, practical people, much more interested in methods than in theories. We'll try anything if it seems to work, if it holds promise of helping our cases. Unfortunately this eagerness also makes us a bit uncritical. Sometimes, we adopt new practices indiscriminately and apply them inappropriately. With only a superficial understanding of the basic information on which the new clinical procedures are based, we administer them unwisely, and then when they do not yield the expected success, we reject the innovations as hastily as we first accepted them. This book is designed to prevent this situation from occurring at least as it relates to modern developments in conditioning therapy with stutterers. We hope to clarify the basic concepts of classical and operant conditioning as they apply to stuttering therapy—and to do so critically. We feel that if we can help the clinician to understand both the nature and limitations of these new ways of helping the stutterer, we can at least prevent a host of harm and perhaps do some real good.

One of our first tasks, therefore, is the job of translation. The psychologists who have spearheaded the development of modern

9

behavioral modification speak and write a language that is foreign to the speech clinician's ears. The words seem abstract and technical, at times almost esoteric. At the possible expense of precision, we shall try to avoid that jargon, to define our terms in ordinary English and to illustrate with clinical examples the things we talk about. Where the jargon cannot be avoided we refer you to the Glossary at the end of the book where many of the terms are defined.

Fortunately, the task is not as difficult as it might appear because speech therapists have been using these "new" concepts and techniques for many years. In the next section of this book, in which we define and discuss them, you will recognize many of them as old friends. For example, you will not be surprised to encounter the technique of relaxation or the use of graded situations (hierarchies) of increasing communicative stress. Surely you have reinforced (rewarded) certain new behaviors and withheld the reinforcement for old responses you wanted to eliminate or change. You know well the advantages and limitations of appropriate penalties and how to work up motivation on the promise of escaping those penalties. Every public school therapist's bag is full of tokens for reinforcement. Speech therapists were using desensitization long before the psychologists discovered the word. All of us have had to shape the speech behaviors of our cases, starting with what they first showed us and progressively modifying it until the client could use it to get reinforcement on his own outside the clinic. All of us have had to deal with anxiety, guilt, and frustration reactions. Indeed, as even this cursory list of examples should indicate, we speech therapists have always been behavior therapists. We use the basic concepts and methods of classical and operant conditioning every day of our professional lives.

Why then do we prepare this booklet? Because we feel strongly that it is better to play by note than by ear if you wish to be a professional. When you do not understand why you do what you do, you do it poorly. Though the science of human behavior is still in its infancy, the infant is growing lustily, and if you continue to ignore it, you will soon reveal yourself as incompetent. Certainly, in this young field of speech pathology, you dare not be content with what you once were taught. If we are to fulfill our dedication, if we are truly to help those we serve, all of us must continue to search for new and better ways of doing our jobs. We grow or we decay.

Basically, what you will find new in behavior modification principles is that they reflect a highly organized and systematic approach to therapy. We speech clinicians have often been accused of relying too much on shotgun therapy—of trying almost anything that might possibly help our cases. In contrast, the behavior therapists insist that we set up reasonable hypotheses and then contrive experiences to test them. They urge us to devise rigorous programs in which the various stimuli, responses, and consequences are clearly specified. They require objective measurement of response strength, not guesswork, and objective criteria of progress, not vague "clinical impressions of improvement." Above all, they demand that we know precisely what we are doing or trying to do when we work with our clients.

And there, of course, lies the rub. Even the experts argue vehemently about the nature of learning and unlearning. What is punishment? Exactly what is being reinforced? Are there different kinds of learning? What are the criteria of successful behavior modification? Hundreds of such basic questions still remain unresolved. Two different behavior therapists will often do the same thing for different reasons, or different things for the same reason. When you meet these differing points of view, you might want to say, "A pox on all your houses" and to stop listening or learning. We hope that you won't react this way when you read this book, though doubtless at times you may be tempted to. The conference which produced this book was not particularly serene despite its setting. Argument and hot rebuttal, criticism and countercriticism were rife at times. But many good dishes have been cooked on the hot fire of controversy and you should find some palatable food for thought in this pot.

Another reaction we suspect you may have will be some initial protest against the methods used by the behavior therapist in the deliberate manipulation of his clients. Most of us have been taught to abhor anything that smacks of brain-washing. We have been told not to try to play God or dictator when hurt people put themselves into our hands. You doubtless have a real respect for the individual's integrity, a faith in his innate potential for self-healing. You would probably say that you prefer to facilitate than manipulate.

The behavior therapists answer your protest by saying that you manipulate your clients whether you want to or not, that you cannot escape doing so no matter what your intentions or philosophy may be. Even the most permissive, client-centered, nondirective therapist reinforces certain client responses more than others. Once the client comes to you for help, and you accept him in that relationship, whatever you do thereafter implies some control by you of his behavior. The behavior therapists would say that, while you might feel more comfortable in the illusion that you can deny your responsibilities for the consequences of your actions by placing much of the burden on your client, this is self-deception and the worst of trickery. They insist that if you are a therapist you will inevitably organize some program of differential reinforcement and administer many of the contingent consequences. Surely, they will say, it is not enough for you merely to preside and hope that something good will happen. To put it bluntly, the behavior therapists tell us that if we think we aren't manipulating our clients, we're just kidding ourselves, that we *are* controlling their behaviors, although we are probably doing it inefficiently and clumsily.

In this book, however, you will find that some of us feel your protest is completely justified. Indeed, one of the reasons we held the conference was to prevent stutterers from being victimized by those who are all too willing to manipulate and control others because of their own ego needs. (May we interject at this point the observation that the kind of therapy you do also shapes the kind of person you become. Therapy is not a one-way process. If you are already a highly authoritarian therapist, perhaps you'd better not do behavior therapy.) Authoritarian people always love the exhilarating but corrupting sense of power. They love to shape that god-stuff called human clay. Though they protest that, if they shock or punish the stutterer when he shows evidence of his frailty, they do so only in the scientific application of learning theory, we have seen the pleasure on their faces as they blew the whistle, pressed the shock key, or said "no, no!"

As therapists, we must also recognize that there are some stutterers who are all too willing to be shaped and manipulated. After all, these sad souls have lived all their lives as puppets dancing from the strings jerked by others, always trying to please, always vulnerable to approval or rejection. These particular stutterers want no responsibility for their own healing. "Tell me what to do!" "Heal me oh Master!" they beg. And there are some who cry "Whip me!" Such stutterers improve very easily, but they relapse fast too. The carryover in improvement once they leave the therapist leaves much to be desired. Again, you will find another group of stutterers who will fiercely resent any attempt on your part to manipulate their behavior. They want freedom, not dependence. They will reject and sabotage you at every turn. Yet another group of stutterers seem to nurse upon anxiety as though it were mother's milk. These verbal sucklings love desensitization hierarchies. They will play the ladder game with you most eagerly, but since they always fall when they approach the final rung, they always win when they lose. Therapists should not play games with human lives.

These remarks are intended to emphasize that behavior modifying procedures are not as simple as they may sound, nor as universally applicable as some have claimed. Anyone who has tried to apply the principles of classical and operant conditioning to stutterers will soon discover not only the complex nature of the disorder but also the wide variability with respect to conditionability, emotional arousal, and many other things. These stuttering clients of ours are not Skinnerian pigeons hatched from laboratory eggs. They are not Pavlovian dogs suspended from experimental frames. They are subject to other controls far more powerful than those we can mobilize in the therapy room. Stutterers come to us with long histories of past conditioning. How they perceive us and what we do to or with them will determine much of the success or failure of our therapy, however it be structured. Speech itself is far more than sequences of segmented motor behaviors. It reflects the person's evaluation of himself and his relationships with others. It is not only emitted by the speaker but evoked by the listener, and there are many listeners whom the therapist cannot control. It is also the vehicle of thought, hope and fear. Stuttering is the dark mirror in which one sees himself distortedly. Behavior therapists have difficulty when they work with stutterers.

So we cannot promise you that behavior therapy will ease your burden or make your work with stutterers easier. If anything, you may have to work harder. Devising appropriate schedules of reinforcements, organizing useful hierarchies, recording stuttering behaviors, and other tasks will take time and effort. You will plague yourself with questions, doubt your clinical judgment, evaluate your skill and competence as never before. But you will find therapy once again to be a fascinating experience and you'll probably be a better therapist for having explored the principles and practices of behavior modification.

PART I

Exposition and Explanation

This section presents two approaches to stuttering therapy. One is based on operant conditioning and the other is based on two-factor learning theory. Our main purpose is to inform, not to persuade, so we have tried to abstain, as far as we could, from criticizing other points of view, though of course no advocate of his own approach can entirely abstain from making his case as strongly as possible. In Part Three of this book we attempt a critical evaluation. This section is to be viewed as exposition and explanation.

Operant Conditioning and Therapy for Stuttering

GEORGE H. SHAMES, Ph.D.

The principles of operant conditioning, developed through research with animals, are now being applied to the human species. We are trying to understand how man learns to behave the way he does. Furthermore, research is now being done on types of behavior that are found only in the human species, such as stuttering. Most of this research on stuttering is aimed at the improvement of clinical skills. Our batting averages with stutterers are not good enough, and to improve them, we must find new techniques of therapy and improve on those techniques already in use. The first step in this process is to become more aware of what is happening in the therapy situation. Are you completely aware of the stutterer's behavior? Are you completely aware of *your* behavior? But most important, are you completely aware of the effect your behavior has on the stutterer's behavior, and incidentally, the effect his behavior has on yours? Whenever you speak, ask questions, smile, or frown, you are probably influencing your client's behavior. The principles of operant conditioning help to explain just how your behavior affects your client's. Knowing how, you will be able to do it more effectively.

I. It's a Matter of Principles: A Common Thread.

The principles of operant conditioning and the techniques of behavior modification, have been applied to stuttering in many different ways. So many, in fact, that you might think that these applications are completely unrelated to one another. This, however, is not the case. There is a common thread binding the "operant people" together. This bond is a belief in a basic principle of behavior. This basic principle is that certain kinds of responses (called operant responses) will occur more or less often, depending on the consequences they generate. If you found a ten dollar bill on your desk every time you wore brown shoes to work, you would shortly wear brown shoes every day of the week. You would probably not be so fussy about your shoes on the weekend, however. Note, then, that it is the consequences of behavior *in certain circumstances* that matter. The circumstances precede the behavior, so that the complete basic principle of operant conditioning is that the events (or stimuli) preceding and following certain types of behavior determine how often they will occur again.

This basic theme may be set down in a shorthand formula that reads: S^D —— R —— Rf. This formula states that a discriminative stimulus (S^D) is the occasion during which a response (R) was reinforced (Rf). Because of the reinforcing event, the S^D becomes associated with the response. As a result, the S^D is said to "control" the occurrence of R because R will consistently follow it. It is this simple principle that is shared by operant researchers and clinicians.

II. Controversy and Conciliation

Those of you who have read some of the literature or heard lectures on operant conditioning and stuttering will know that there is much controversy and debate surrounding the subject. Our discussion will take on more perspective if we look briefly at the nature of the disagreements that make up this debate. Very likely, the most important disagreement with the operant approach to stuttering is that it deals solely with observable behaviors. The focus on observable behaviors probably reflects the experimental, laboratory heritage from which operant conditioning techniques are derived.

In the laboratory, the researcher must be absolutely precise in describing and defining the responses under investigation. To meet these requirements, the experimenter must restrict himself to observable stimuli and responses. Furthermore, the researcher must be able to quantify what he can observe; he cannot simply report his casual impressions. It is only through such rigorously scientific and painstaking research that we are able to draw decisive conclusions about our ability to experimentally modify behavior under controlled conditions.

For you the clinician, however, these rigorously objective activities, such as actually counting different types of responses, or scheduling yourself for only certain types of reactions, are procedures that may be not only foreign but repugnant. Furthermore, these activities may close the door on a number of clinical styles and on a number of stuttering theories. Clinicians, for example, like to think that they are treating the whole person, not just one small fragment of behavior. Also, they want to be free to deal with anything they think is relevant and deal with it as it arises during the clinical session, instead of having to deal only with what has been designated beforehand as the response under consideration. Clinicians also want the freedom to respond when and how they see fit instead of having to respond with a smile here, a wrinkled brow there according to a preprogrammed schedule of response-contingent events.

Although these different activities may look like freedoms to the clinician, they look like inconsistency to the operant conditioner, and furthermore, he would be nearly certain that such inconsistency would render successful conditioning next to impossible. This may be the most important lesson taught us by the operant laboratories—that consistently applied preprogrammed schedules of contingent events are the most effective way of achieving behavior change. Of course, for the clinician, being programmed to a schedule of activity minimizes his human judgment, and judgment is one of the clinician's most valuable possessions and is not to be idly tossed aside. Perhaps some compromise is possible between judgment and freedom on the one hand and consistency on the other. The wise clinician knows when, during an interview, it is time to be inconsistent and to shift away from the preprogrammed activity to something that is more meaningful at that moment. Such judgments, however, will be exercised with care by the wise clinician, for both he and the stutterer may have invested considerable time, thought, and examination to the schedule so abandoned.

There are also many who wonder how relevant operant conditioning is when it does not deal, at least not to the satisfaction of many, with such things as the stutterer's attitudes, feelings, emotions, and all of the other usually private aspects of stuttering. Most of us agree that these private aspects are part of the problem, but the operantly oriented people, according to this argument, see stuttering as merely the frequency of its overt occurrence, nothing more.

Finally, many clinicians do not like to think of themselves as manipulators of someone else's behavior. They like to think that the person is helping himself, directing himself, realizing his own potential for his own good. It is difficult to hold this view and at the same time arrange programs to systematically alter someone else's behavior.

Operant clinicians realize that most of the work done so far on this subject has been research, rather than tried and true procedures for therapy. The purpose of this research, however, is to develop therapy procedures that are both valid and effective and based on logical principles of behavior modification supported by reliable and valid research data.

This research has resulted in a number of suggestions and speculations about the prevention of stuttering and therapy for stuttering. There has, however, been very little published information about clinical applications. The operant clinicians, however, are quick to point out that there is also little data supporting the effectiveness of the more traditional therapies for stuttering. The operant researchers feel that the tactics of how to apply their research results in the clinic should be left to the clinician's artistry. There is no longer any question of whether the clinician is a manipulator of behavior. He is already manipulating behavior; the question is how good a manipulator can he become. In answer to those who criticize operant conditioning for not dealing with unobservable attitudes and feelings, operant conditioners feel that unless the stutterer's speech behavior is improved, the other things that may happen to him during therapy are of questionable value as far as therapy for stuttering is concerned, although they may have other benefits. Operant conditioners also feel strongly that unless the clinician restricts himself to observable behaviors, he may think a therapeutic technique is successful and continue to use it with stutterers when in fact it has had no effect at all. Because of the influence of the observer's bias, his wish for the client to improve, it is impossible to be certain that change has taken place when unobservable events are being dealt with.

Operant conditioners want it known that although the work so far has been experimental that does not mean that operant applications to stuttering must be limited to electro mechanical laboratory demonstrations. Instead, operant conditioning should be extended to the field and to the social environment of the stutterer. There is no reason why the real-life encounters of the stutterer cannot be brought within the operant framework, provided it is done in a systematic way. In this regard, note that there really is no operant conditioning theory of stuttering; operant conditioning is simply a strategy for achieving behavior change. The strategy needs only to be filled in with some content. Something is to be modified—but what? The answer depends on the stutterers, the clinicians, and perhaps the theorists. It should be clear that a strategy of manipulation does not tell us specifically what is to be manipulated. The specific forms of the behaviors to be manipulated can be derived from any content theory of stuttering, as long as the parts of that theory can be related to observable events.

On the other side of the coin, those who favor operant conditioning and behavior modification, as compared to the more traditional therapies, feel that the stutterer is sold short when he is asked at the beginning of therapy to accept his stuttering and to learn to live with it or to modify it into a more socially acceptable form. The goal for the operant conditioner is speech that is free of what we commonly call stuttering. This goal may or may not be realistic—only research and clinical application will provide an answer, but this difference in the goal of therapy is a profound one.

III.   Therapy as Operant Conditioning: A Variable Process

We have said that, according to the basic principle of operant conditioning, a behavior will occur more or less often depending on the consequences it generates. What is meant, in this context, by the word *consequence?* A consequence is an event that will occur if and only if some target behavior has been emitted by the subject. Since the occurrence of the consequence depends directly on the occurrence of the target behavior, the consequence is called a "contingent" event.

When we say that consequences, or contingent events, modify someone's behavior, we mean that certain aspects of that behavior have been made to occur either more or less often as a result of the consequences they generated. So there are two directions modification can take—it can cause the behavior to occur more often or it can cause the behavior to occur less often. For each of these two directions that modification can take, there are several procedures for achieving it.

A simple diagram is the easiest way to present these procedures and the concepts that underlie them. In the center of Figure 1, there is a large capital R. Let this R stand for the large number of forms that stuttering responses can take—forms such as syllable repetitions, prolongations, sound repetitions, whole word repetitions, phrase repetitions, interjections, etc. The operant worker usually avoids

S^D		Rf+
S^Δ	R ————→	Rf—
		Extinction
S^A	Stuttering	Punishment
	Responses	
Preceding		Following
Events	Figure 1	Events

terms such as "starters," "releasers," "postponement devices," "avoidance behaviors," etc., because they interpret the function of the behavior rather than simply describe it. R can also include what have come to be called secondary behaviors in the stuttering jargon. Consequently, R may include pressing the lips together, taking a deep breath, adducting the vocal chords, forcing the tongue into pressure postures, etc. R may also include secondary behaviors involving other parts of the body, such as foot-tapping, finger-drumming, eyeblinking, head-shaking, knee-slapping, etc. R may also include topics of conversation which reflect the stutterer's perception and evaluation of himself, his attitudes about his speaking, about his listeners, or about anything else in his environment. R may also include underlying physiological processes, such as those measured by GSR and EKG. R can, in fact, stand for any event that we have agreed to call stuttering behavior, or that we feel is relevant to the problem of stuttering, provided that event is an observable one.

To the right of the R there are four possible events which could occur as consequences to a response. These four types of events could represent the therapist's behavior as he tries to modify a stutterer's speech or social behavior. Rf+ and Rf— refer to a procedure known as reinforcement, which can take both positive and negative forms. Both types of reinforcement are procedures which increase the frequency of the responses they follow. An example might be something as simple as the therapist saying "good," or nodding and smiling in an approving manner right after the stutterer has reported that he approached a feared talking situation, or after he has deliberately modified some motor aspect of his stuttering. This would be an example of a positive reinforcer. In this case, in positive reinforcement, a stimulus is presented. In negative reinforcement, a stimulus is taken away. For example, if a stuttering child is afraid to talk to his father because of negative reactions on the father's part, the therapist might ask the father to stop reacting in that way so that the child would speak to the father more often. Note that in both types of reinforcement the behavior occurs more often. It might seem, at first glance, that positive reinforcement is like rewarding the stutterer or doing something pleasant to him, while negative reinforcement is taking away something unpleasant. The difficulty with these terms is that human beings, and in fact other animals as well, are so complicated that one can never be sure in advance what will be pleasant or unpleasant to any given individual. Consequently, operant workers do not usually identify an event as a reinforcer until after they have seen it work, that is, until after they have actually seen it increase the frequency of the behavior on which it was contingent. In both of the examples of reinforcement, given above, the reinforcing event took place in the stutterer's external environment. This may be the method with a child stutterer. For an adult stutterer, however, many of the consequences of his behavior come from within himself in the form of self-evaluations, sensations of tension, etc. In the case of the adult, then, the therapist may well focus on changing internal consequences rather than external ones.

Another event that may follow R is the weakening or extinction of a response. The procedure for achieving this end is simply the removal of a reinforcer. As a technique for modifying stuttering behavior, extinction is often ineffective. The difficulty is that in order to weaken a response by withdrawing its reinforcer, the reinforcer withdrawn must be the same one that was maintaining the behavior in the first place. In operant jargon, the response must be "under the control" of the reinforcer. Since you cannot weaken through extinction what you do not control through reinforcement, and since the complicated and changing reinforcements for any human behavior are frequently unidentifiable, it is usually impossible to discover what reinforcer to withdraw in order to extinguish a stuttering behavior. We have all, however, seen those stutterers who have learned to profit by their stuttering. In these cases, it is sometimes possible to identify the reinforcements in the environment which may be at least partly responsible for some of the stutterer's behavior. In such cases, we do our best to extinguish what we can.

Punishment is another kind of event that can follow a response. Punishment interrupts or depresses responses. As with reinforcement, we do not like to conclude that an event is a punisher until we have actually seen it interrupt or depress a response. Punishment has probably been used in therapy more often than we like to think. When a clinician instructs a stutterer to repeat a stuttered word, he may be punishing him by delaying his communication. Therapists may punish too by shaking their heads, disagreeing, saying "no," or even "I don't understand." Silence too may be punishing.

There are therefore four different kinds of consequent events to a response. Positive and negative reinforcement, which cause a behavior to occur more often, and extinction and punishment, which cause a behavior to occur less often. In all cases, the events may occur in the stutterer's external environment or be internal and self-produced.

The symbol S^D in Figure 1 to the left of R indicates an event that takes place before the response occurs. This kind of antecedent event is called a discriminative stimulus, and it means a specific aspect of the total stimulus situation preceding the occurrence of the response that has come to be associated with the reinforcement of that response. These events serve as cues, indicating that particular responses will be reinforced. In a sense, then, the S^D signals to the subject that a response occurring at this time will be reinforced.

The symbol S^Δ is also to the left of the R and therefore occurs before the response. This symbol also refers to a cue, that is, a signal with a discriminitive function, but in this case the stimulus signals that reinforcement will not follow. Finally, the third event that may precede the response, S^A, stands for a stimulus that signals to the subject that an aversive consequence will follow. A teacher may become such a stimulus if she consistently punishes a child for stuttering. This type of stimulus may bring on not only instrumental avoidance responses, such as complete silence, but it may also bring on emotional activity, which interferes with the operant behavior of fluent speech. S^D, S^Δ, and S^A, by repeatedly occurring before a response associated with a particular consequence, come to control the frequency of the responses they precede. As a result the S^D is likely to cause a response to occur more often, while the S^Δ, and the S^A are likely to cause a response to occur less often.

These different techniques or procedures for modifying the frequency with which responses occur are often called strategies. These different strategies, the different events that may be used in each of them and the different responses they may be used to modify, are set forth in Table 1.

These strategies do not have to be used one at a time, and, in fact, they are often used in combination with each other. They can be found in many different forms, and they have been used with a variety of different responses. In some instances they have only been laboratory demonstrations, while in others they have been used as clinical therapeutic techniques. Sometimes, what was

Table 1.

Response by Stutterer	Strategies	Possible Contingent Events
Fluent speech		Verbal approval
Modifying the form of stuttering		Smiling
Approach behavior	Positive reinforcement (contingent event increasing the frequency of response)	Affirmation head nodding
Increasing verbal output		Agreeing, etc.
Comments compatible with changing stuttering (e.g. indicating a desire to work on problem)		
An interruption of stuttering		Termination of disapproval
Voluntary and controlled stuttering which interrupts stuttering.	Negative reinforcement (A contingent event increasing the frequency of the response)	Termination of the stutterer's negative evaluation
		Termination of the sensation of muscular tension
Stuttering		Attention, formerly offered, is withheld
Comments incompatible with modifying stuttering (e.g. reflecting helplessness, victimization, non behavioral interpretations of behavior	Extinction (The withdrawal of a positive reinforcer weakening the response)	Agreement is withheld
		Approval is withdrawn
		Release from oral activity is no longer available
		Rejection of stuttering as an excuse for failure
Stuttering	Punishment	Electric shock
Comments incompatible with modifying stuttering	(A contingent event weakening the response)	Verbal disapproval preventing continuation of communication

originally designed to be a laboratory demonstration resulted by accident in a technique for therapy. In other cases, however, and very often by design, the laboratory demonstration remains a demonstration with no resulting clinical application. Such demonstrations are not valueless simply because they have no clinical application, since they stimulate further research and increase our understanding of stuttering. In this discussion, however, we will restrict our considerations to the techniques of operant conditioning that have been applied to stuttering therapy.

IV. Some Specific Applications

A. DAF and a New Speech Response

Under normal conditions of talking, there is practically no delay in the feedback of our speech activity—we hear and feel ourselves talk almost simultaneously. As this auditory and kinesthetic feedback continuously informs us that our utterance is proceeding as intended, we continue to talk. When the auditory portion of speech feedback is delayed, however, this timing is disrupted. In delayed auditory feedback a speaker will not proceed to a sound until he is certain, by both hearing and feeling it, that he has actually produced the preceding sound. This waiting for confirmation produces a delayed pattern of speaking. The delayed pattern can either be a series of silences or a prolongation and continuation of the sound until auditory feedback has been received. When a stutterer experiences delayed auditory feedback, the same pattern of slow and prolonged speech that is seen in normals appears.(2). This pattern of speech is incompatible with the motor aspects of stuttering. The first goal of this kind of therapy is the firm establishment of the nonstuttering, prolonged pattern of speaking. In this case, the procedure for achieving that firm establishment is called an "elimination-avoidance" procedure. The stutterer reads out loud while conditions of delayed auditory feedback are continuously maintained. If the client should stutter, however, DAF is terminated for 10 seconds, and he continues to read without DAF. By continuing to produce the prolonged type of speech, and consequently by not stuttering, the client "avoids" having the DAF cut off. Once this prolonged type of speech is established, DAF is gradually faded out of the situation. At this point the stutterer is reading with his prolonged type of speech without any DAF. A tachistoscope, which systematically varies the speed with which the reading material is presented, is now introduced. With the aid of this instrument, the stutterer increases his reading speed and at the same time develops conversational phrasing. If, during this phase of increasing the rate, stuttering should occur, the procedure is backed up so that reading rate is slowed down. As soon as nonstuttered speech is re-established, the reading rate is again increased. If backing up to a slower rate is not successful in removing stuttering, the procedure is backed up further, and DAF is reintroduced until the slow prolonged, nonstuttering speech pattern is more firmly established. In the final phase of this technique, when speech free of stuttering is occurring at normal conversational speed, self-control procedures are taught. With these procedures, the stutterer tries to change his environment in a way that will be most likely to bring about a change in his speech and social behavior.

Note that in this procedure the goal of therapy is speech that is free of stuttering. There is no attempt to introduce and maintain a different form of stuttering. Instead the purpose is to establish and substitute a completely new speech response (the prolonged pattern of speech). This new pattern is first established, then shaped into an appropriate conversational form. We would expect this form to be maintained by those factors in the environment that reinforce fluency for all of us, probably the social reinforcement of our listeners.

It is difficult to assess the success of this technique since the reports of the social carryover of the fluent speech pattern acquired in the laboratory have been only anecdotal. These reports have been less precise than the frequency counts and descriptive detail that have characterized the laboratory activities.

B.   Instrumental Punishment as a Therapeutic Procedure.

Some authors have strongly suggested that punishment might be a very effective clinical tactic. Their work has shown that when electric shock or the words "wrong," or "not good" are contingent on stuttering behaviors, those behaviors occur less often. Furthermore, they have stated that the verbal approval (Rf+) of fluency does not produce more fluency.

Many clinicians and theorists object strongly to the suggestion that punishment should be used in the clinic. Many such clinicians have been trained in the theory that stuttering evolves from the punishment of normal dysfluency. How then, they ask, can punishment both beget stuttering and suppress it? One answer to this argument is that the responses on which punishment is contingent are different in the two cases. It is possible, then, that the punishment of *normal dysfluency* may produce stuttering while at the same time the punishment of *stuttering* may suppress it.

Others who object to the suggestion that punishment should be used in the clinic may not like to think of themselves as purveyors of punishment, even though it may be for the stutterer's ultimate good and well-being. It may be, however, that some of these same clinicians are already punishing their clients in other ways. For example, they may confront the stutterer with his behavior, either verbally, or by having him look in a mirror. They may raise semantic

26

questions about the way he talks about his stuttering. They may literally force their clients to talk in feared situations, under the threat of being dismissed from the clinic. They may ask the stutterer to repeat a stuttered word, thereby delaying his message and his social reinforcement. They may do all these things under the banner of therapy, without calling them punishment. Do these tactics become less acceptable if they are called punishment? The important question is whether these tactics are effective in treating stuttering. In this light, the laboratory data suggest that they might be more effective if they were administered on a consistent schedule as a consequence of some predesignated behavior of the client's.

It is unfortunate that the authors of these experiments have chosen to underplay the fact that once punishment is removed, stuttering again increases. Consequently, it may well be that punishment alone is not clinically effective, but that when it is used in combination with positive reinforcement (approval), so that the stutterer has an alternative response available, it is effective in modifying stuttering.

C. Applying Operant Techniques to Traditional Therapies

Many traditional techniques for treating stuttering have been systematized within the operant framework to see if more consistent reinforcement practices might make them more effective.

One traditional technique is composed of three phases—establishment, transfer and maintenance of fluency. Within each of these phases, the stutterer reads, speaks in monologue, and converses under instruction to "prolong" any word he expects to stutter on and to repeat in a "prolonging" style each word he actually stutters. Positive reinforcement in the form of verbal approval is given for fluent speech as well as for the prolonging pattern. In this phase a pattern of fluent speech is established.

In the transfer phase, the situation is gradually made more complex. The idea is to transfer the newly acquired pattern from the simplicity of the clinic to the complexity of every-day life. Consequently, the size of the audience is gradually increased, and the conversational situation is gradually made more complicated in a number of different ways.

In the maintenance phase, the client comes less and less often to the clinic. At the same time, he is trained to take on more of the responsibility for his behavior until eventually he is completely on his own.

In this treatment program, the target response is the overt, observable stuttering on a word, and the goal is to reduce the number of times such stutterings happen. Once this goal has been achieved in the clinic, it is necessary to change the stimulus control (S^D) over stuttering by varying the situation, audiences, and conversational settings that have come to evoke stuttering in the past. To achieve this, the therapist systematically substitutes one stimulus for another (mother for therapist, real phone for play phone, etc.). Each of these stimuli becomes the situation for the stutterer to emit his newly acquired fluent speech behavior. Changing stimulus control is probably aided by the process of stimulus generalization, in which stimulus situations similar to those worked on in the clinic also come to control the occurrence of fluent speech outside the clinic. The transfer of stimulus control is also aided by having the therapist (the original source of reinforcement) participate in some limited way in the progressively complex situations.

The final steps of this carryover procedure, however, are left to the stutterer to work out with his environment, as support from the clinic and the therapist is gradually faded. At this point previous work in therapy should have established in the stutterer a new pattern of self-evaluation, and self-perception, and a new way of perceiving his audience that will provide reinforcement for his newly acquired behavior and maintain it even as external support is withdrawn.

Another traditional technique has used the interview as a vehicle for therapy. A review of clinical stuttering therapy sessions has revealed two general, but not necessarily exclusive, types of stutterers. One type shows a great many struggle behaviors, which often interfere with intelligibility or disrupt grammatical integrity enough to impair communication severely. The other type of stutterer is distinguished primarily by what he says rather than by the way he says it, and his communication is not severely impaired. For each of these two types of stutterer a different type of therapy program has been developed. One deals primarily with the symptom or struggle components of stuttering (for example, repetitions and prolongations), and the second deals with the thematic content of what the stutterer says.

The program designed to modify the struggle behaviors make use of verbal consequences as stimuli. Using a shaping procedure, the therapist at first reinforces the stutterer for modifying his stuttering in almost any way. As the program progresses, however, he is reinforced for behaviors approaching fluency. Gradually, the therapist reinforces only those behaviors that approximate fluency more closely. This procedure, in which more desirable behaviors are selectively reinforced while less desirable ones are extinguished, is called differential reinforcement. Reinforcers that have been found to be effective in this and other verbal conditioning research include "good," "okay," "mmhmm," "that's good," and so on. Verbal disapproval for failure to respond in the desired manner has also been used in other programs, separately and in combination with approval.

What follows is a step-by-step outline of the procedures used in this program:

In step 1, the stutterer is asked to pause after every stuttered word and to repeat the word, after which he is reinforced by the clinician. Saying a stuttered word again, even if it is stuttered the second time too, is considered a correct response provided the stutterer repeats the word before going on to the next word. To separate the word-repetition that is a stuttering behavior from the word-repetition that is part of the program, a correct response is defined as a stuttered word, followed by a pause, followed by an additional utterance of the word.

Step 2 is a refinement of step 1. The stutterer receives reinforcement if he repeats a stuttered word and also prolongs the first sound of the word, for example, "m-m-m-man (pause) mmman."

In step 3, the stutterer is reinforced when he stops himself while stuttering on a word and prolongs the first sound of the word being stuttered, for example, "m-m- (pause) mmman." The prolongation of the initial sound of the word following the whole word repetition is also considered a correct response, for example, "not, not (pause), nnnot."

In step 4, the stutterer is reinforced when he prolongs the first sound of a stuttered word, for example, "mmman." This response is not differentiated from a stuttering prolongation, and both types of response are reinforced. The program may be extended by differentially reinforcing progressively shorter prolongation durations, thus more closely approximating normal speech.

In order to progress from one step to the next in this program the client must successfully complete the required task of each step on 90% of the words stuttered. When the 90% criterion is reached, the stutterer proceeds to the next step. Once the stutterer has progressed to the next step, he is no longer reinforced for the response required for an earlier step. The client and the clinician agree upon the theme of the discussion before the session begins. This helps prevent long silent periods and reduces the probability of emotionally loaded themes. Table 2 summarizes this program for modifying the motor aspects of stuttering.

There are, however, a number of theorists who maintain that the motor aspects of stuttering are only symptoms of an underlying disorder. Some feel that stuttering may be maintained to a great degree as a result of the concepts the stutterer possesses. For example, stutterers often regard themselves as the victims of nonobservable entities, such as being helpless, being under the irreversible control of past events, and so on. Certain content themes have been identified as characteristic of stutterers from observations on their language. Two broad response classes have been categorized because of their frequency in the language of stutterers and because

29

Table 2. Summary of Steps in Stuttering Behavior Program

Program Step	Client's Task	Clinician's Contingent Responses	
		Positive Reinforcement	Punishment for failure to Complete Task
1	Pause following every stuttered word and repeat the word.	"Good," "fine," that's good," "okay," mm-hm," head nod, etc.	Interrupt client and repeat task instructions.
2	Repeat the stuttered word prolonging its initial sound	Same	Same
3	Interrupt stuttering on a word and prolong its initial sound.	Same	Same
4	Prolong the first sound of each stuttered word.	Same	Same

of their assumed relationship to stuttering: (1) utterances that are considered beneficial to therapy—called positive language content responses, and (2) utterances considered incompatible with recovery—called negative language content responses.

Based on these two categories of responses, programs have been established to modify the thematic content of stutterers' utterances. The idea is to strengthen the positive themes and weaken the negative ones. Table 3 lists ten types of statement. Usually, categories 1-8 are considered positive, while 9 and 10 are negative. There are exceptions, however. For example, category 6, Negative Affect, may be positive or negative depending on the individual stutterer and the context in which it occurs.

Three different content modification programs have been developed so far. These programs are listed in Table 4. In all of these programs verbal approval is used to reinforce desirable content. In programs 1 and 3, however, mild verbal punishment is also used to weaken the occurrence of undesirable content. Also, in program 1, the clinician is programmed to help the stutterer increase his verbal output. Program 2, which uses verbal approval alone, was designed for the stutterer who does not need to weaken undesirable responses because such responses do not occur very often to begin with, but who does need to have desirable responses strengthened because they do not occur often enough. The third program was designed for stutterers who have a large number of

Table 3. Positive and Negative Thematic Content Response Categories.

Response Category	Definition	Example
1. Concurrent Variables	Statements which reflect client's awareness or growing awareness of events or situations which accompany his stuttering or fluency.	"I stutter when I'm talking on the phone," or "I don't stutter much around home."
2. Controlling Variables	Statements which reflect client's awareness or growing awareness of events which control or cause his stuttering behavior or fluency.	Maybe I stutter because I think about how I'm going to talk before I say anything."
3. Description of Struggle Behavior	Statements which describe a client's overt motor struggle behavior when speaking.	"I blink my eyes when I stutter."
4. Description of Avoidance Behavior	Statements which describe or report a client's avoidance behavior at word, situation, and interpersonal levels.	"I sometimes change words when I think I'm going to stutter."
5. Positive Affect	Statements which describe or evaluate a client's feelings or emotional state in a positive manner.	"It makes me feel good not to stutter."
6. Negative Affect	Statements which describe or evaluate a client's feelings or emotional state in a negative manner.	"I sometimes hate everybody in the world."
7. Contemplated Action	Statements which report the contemplation of engaging in activities or meeting situations which involve speaking.	"I think I'll call him on the phone tonight."
8. Completed Action	Statements which report the completion of action involving speaking.	"I finally talked to my boss today about the raise."
9. Ambiguous Amorphous Entities	Statements referring to speech or stuttering which are imprecise, vague, or nondescriptive. Must contain the key words *it, this, or this thing.*	"It occurs when I start to talk." Or, "I just don't know what to do about this thing."
10. Helplessness Victimization	Statements reflecting client's perceptions of stuttering as an event which renders him helpless, incapable of acting, or as being the victim of outside events over which he has no control.	"I can't get the word out." "I'm just not able to say it." "When this stuttering happens, the word gets caught and I can't get it out."

undesirable content responses but very few desirable content responses. What follows is an example of the first of these three programs.

Table 4. Summary of Thematic Content Modification Program

Program	Target Response	Clinician's Behavior
1	Positive and negative statements	Positively reinforce positive statements Punish negative statements Intervene noncontingently to maintain client's verbal output
2	Positive statements	Positively reinforce positive statement
3	Positive and negative statements	Positively reinforce positive statements Punish negative statements

In this program the clinician reinforces positive statements and punishes negative ones, and, at the same time, uses additional statements that are delivered noncontingently in order to increase verbal behavior in general. When reinforcing a positive statement, the clinician repeats or paraphrases the statement, and then adds a phrase of approval, such as "I understand," "I see," "you're right," "okay," "good," or "mmhmm." Similarly, he paraphrases or repeats negative statements and adds a phrase of disapproval, such as "I don't understand," "No," "I don't agree," or "That's not right." The clinician replies noncontingently, that is, without regard to content, with statements such as "Can you tell me more?" or "Is there anything else?" No instructions are given to the client before or during the program. This program was designed for stutterers whose speech was intelligible and grammatically intact but whose verbal output requires occasional stimulation.

Sample utterances by the stutterer and the clinician are:

Stutterer: I stutter less when I am around my family or people who know me well.

Clinician: When you are around your family or people you know, you don't stutter as much. I see. (Judging that the stutterer's statement fit the definition of a concurrent variable, positive statement. See Table 3, category 1.)

Stutterer: This sound won't come out.

Clinician: This sound won't come out. I don't understand. (Judging

32

the statement as one reflecting helplessness-victimization, a negative category. See Table 3, category 10.)

In addition to these operant programs which either modify the form of stuttering or modify the content of what stutterers talk about, there are also programs which reinforce fluency and punish stuttering, through verbal approval and disapproval during conversations. Such a program is used when stuttering occurs on less than 5 percent of the words spoken, often after the stutterer has completed one of the modification programs (language content and/or motor form).

In this program, the clinician makes a statement of approval, such as "good" or "fine" immediately following the first fluent word following 15 seconds of fluency. When such 15-second periods of fluency have been established well enough to make up half of the client's talking time during the interview, verbal disapproval or punishment for each instance of stuttering is introduced as a supplement to reinforcement. When this combination of consequences has resulted in fluent speech for half of the interview, the criterion for reinforcement is changed to 30 seconds of fluent speech. As soon as the 30-second periods of fluency make up half of the interview time, the criterion is changed to one minute of fluency. In all cases, verbal disapproval contingent on a moment of stuttering is used only after the stutterer has demonstrated that he can be fluent for the duration of the period of time in use during half of the time he speaks. When the stutterer reaches the one minute criterion, he is put into a group of stutterers who are at the same stage of fluency. Members of the group then take over the punishing and reinforcing roles of the therapist.

Conclusion

For the clinician, operant conditioning suggests that he become alert to the possibilities of behavioral principles. They may have value for him. He should know that his own behavior—when he smiles or looks up at the window, pays attention, or disapproves—affects the stutterer and the course of his therapy. Sometimes what the therapist does has little effect because the stutterer is listening to himself, evaluating himself, cursing himself, or deceiving himself, permitting little or no intrusion by the therapist. But at other times, what the therapist does, perhaps without thinking, can profoundly affect the course of therapy.

At any one instant, the stutterer is being controlled by many things—by his history of rewards and punishments, by a number of past and current events, people, hair color, physiological sensations, fatigue, social interaction, and so on, as well as by the immediate listener. Consequently, we should not feel too self important in our roles as therapists or about the effects of our behavior. In all probability, the real battleground, where the basic changes and insights take place, where thoughts and feelings are exposed, the real arena of confrontation, is in the self-examination, in the inventory-taking, and in the probing that the stutterer does inside of himself as he thinks and feels and reacts to his own thoughts and feelings. The therapist can help in this personal activity of the client's by arranging the climate for it with appropriate questions and interpretations. The therapist can prod for deeper self-examination, he can encourage changes in speech and social behavior, he can instruct and he can approve or disapprove of the client's attempts. All of these things can be placed within the framework of the principles of operant conditioning. Ultimately, however, the stutterer learns to prod himself, to encourage himself, to interpret, and to approve and disapprove on his own. In short he becomes responsible for himself. This is what the wise therapist is constantly striving to accomplish with his stutterers.

The research data and the experimental therapy techniques described in this chapter are not yet sophisticated enough or relevant enough for anyone to suggest to the clinician that he should throw away his most prized possession, his clinical judgment, and his personal clinical style and artistry, so that he can be programmed into a set of nonjudgmental and only partially valid activities. Such programming is the method of the researcher. It is a method which the researcher hopes will turn up valuable information for the clinician. The principles of operant behavior may even now be carefully and selectively applied by the knowledgable clinician to therapy for the stutterer. The idea that stuttering can be manipulated in part by the consequences provided by a therapist may help the clinician to organize his therapy, and may even suggest specific clinical techniques. But, with these principles tucked away close by and available for application, sound clinical judgment is still the rule for clinicians.

Additional Readings

Carrier, J., Shames, G. H., and Egolf, D. B., "The Design and Application of an Experimental Therapy Program for Stutterers." A paper presented at the Annual Convention of the American Speech and Hearing Association, Chicago, November 1969.

Goldiamond, I., "Stuttering and Fluency as Manipulatable Operant Response Classes," in Sloane, H. W., and MacAulay, B. D. (Eds.), *Operant Procedures in Remedial Speech and Language Training.* Boston: Houghton Mifflin, 1968.

Martin, R., "The Experimental Manipulation of Stuttering Behaviors," in Sloane, H. W., and MacAulay, B. D. (Eds.), *Operant Procedures in Remedial Speech and Language Training.* Boston: Houghton Mifflin, 1968.

Ryan, B., "The Establishment, Transfer, and Maintenance of Fluent Reading and Speaking in a Stutterer Using Operant Technology." A paper presented at the Annual Convention of the American Speech and Hearing Association, Denver, November 1968.

Shames, G. H., Egolf, D. B., and Rhodes, R. C., "Experimental Programs in Stuttering Therapy." *Journal of Speech and Hearing Disorders*, February 1969, pp. 30-47.

Two-Factor Behavior Theory and Therapy

GENE J. BRUTTEN, Ph.D.

BEHAVIOR THEORY

Life would be much simpler for the therapist if all behaviors were learned and unlearned in the same way. More often than not, however, experience has led learning theorists away from such one-factor explanations. They know that learning can result from two, quite different conditioning procedures—classical conditioning, which is also called respondent conditioning, and instrumental conditioning, which is also called operant conditioning. When a therapist wants to modify a particular behavior, he can do so most efficiently if he can determine whether that behavior was originally learned by classical or by instrumental conditioning. Although some therapeutic techniques are effective on both classical and instrumental responses, most techniques are effective only on the appropriate class of behavior.

Recently, behavorial scientists have focussed on instrumental responses, like the word-changing and arm-swinging of stutterers, but they are still fully aware of the classically conditioned responses, such as the emotional reactions seen so often in stutterers. This recent focus on instrumental responses is probably just another example of the pendulum of scientific popularity swinging from one emphasis to the next.

Classical Conditioning

At the turn of the century, Pavlov created a great deal of excitement with his experiments on classical conditioning. Pavlov observed that there were two different types of stimuli. One type of stimulus was always followed by a specific response. For example, if a dog's paw was shocked electrically, the dog would always lift his paw up. Or, if food were presented to a hungry dog, he would salivate. Pavlov called these stimuli *unconditional stimuli* and the reflexive responses that followed them *unconditional responses*, because the relationship between them was unconditionally present, that is, it did not depend on learning. Through a slight mistranslation, they have come to be called unconditioned stimuli and unconditioned responses. The other type of stimulus that Pavlov observed was not associated, like the unconditioned stimulus, with a particular response. Such stimuli as a ringing bell or a red light would usually produce no more than a casual glance from the subject. For obvious reasons, these stimuli have come to be called neutral stimuli. By experimenting with different arrangements of these two types of

37

stimuli, Pavlov found that when the unconditioned stimulus was made consistently contingent on the neutral stimulus, the neutral stimulus would eventually come to evoke a response similar to the unconditioned response. This new response was called the conditioned response, and the originally neutral stimulus was called the conditioned stimuli.

In the traditional example of classical conditioning, a neutral stimulus like a tone is presented, followed by an unconditioned stimulus, like an intense shock. From previous observation it is known that the intense shock will produce a number of different arousal behaviors. After the shock has been contingent on the tone for a number of trials, the subject eventually begins to show some form of arousal or excitation after the tone occurs *but before the shock occurs,* or even if the shock does not occur. Once these arousal behaviors occur before the shock, classical conditioning has taken place. The subject has come to respond to the tone in a way that is similar to his response to the shock. He responds to the tone as if it were a sign of the impending shock. He has learned that when the tone occurs, shock is likely to follow.

Simple as the procedure sounds, classical conditioning is not limited to the training of lower animals like dogs, mice, or pigeons. The same results are obtained with humans. Furthermore, this procedure is not limited to laboratory stimuli, like a tone or a light. Any stimulus that an organism can see, hear, feel, or taste can be classically conditioned. A person, a word, or an entire stimulus situation may be classically conditioned. This is true of stutterers and nonstutterers alike. All of us, in fact, have experienced a conditioned emotional response to originally neutral stimuli. Bugs, supervisory personnel, heights, water, teachers, and mice are some of the neutral stimuli that can come to arouse us through classical conditioning.

Because of our own similar experiences, we should be able to understand the classically conditioned emotional response of stutterers. You have undoubtedly seen many stutterers for whom initially neutral stimuli have come, through experience, to evoke negative emotion—a certain word, a particular sound, words that begin a sentence, or words that are longer than average, are examples. Many stutterers report that particular listeners, their age, sex, or number, the topic of conversation, the specific setting, or the feel of a particular articulatory posture or movement, evoke a negative emotional response. These stimuli consistently make them uncomfortable, afraid, or anxious. Their hearts pound, their muscles are tense, their hands sweat, and their breathing becomes irregular. Furthermore, the emotional response is usually associated with fluency failure. Negative emotional responding seems to interfere with the accuracy and continuity of motor performance that is so vital to fluent speech. It's hard to speak fluently—in fact it's hard to perform any fine motor act—when the body is under stress and functioning less than perfectly. The result is a disrupted and disorganized performance. We have all had this experience. We all remember—perhaps even with some wistfulness—the ungainly way we tripped and sputtered on our first date, with our first client, or meeting our future in-laws. The experience of stutterers are not unusual. What is unusual is that they are *consistently* aroused by specific words and specific speech situations that are not objectively dangerous and that do not concern most people. A stutterer's experiences do not generally diminish the emotional reaction, they often make it worse. The negative emotional reaction to words and situations generally become more consistent and so too does the consequent stuttering.

Classical conditioning is not limited to a *negative* emotional response. Neutral stimuli may also be contingently followed by stimuli that are positive or pleasant. The sounds of mother's speech and the sight of her face may come to elicit a positive emotional response in an infant because these neutral stimuli are consistently associated with being fed (unconditioned stimulus). Eventually, the baby has a positive emotional response when he sees his mother approaching the crib. For the stutterer, as for anyone else, many stimuli have come to arouse positive emotional reactions. On certain sounds and words and under certain circumstances they have little or no difficulty. Many stutterers, even severe ones, are fluent when they are with a girl friend, out with the boys, or reading a passage from a book. Positive emotion facilitates the normal fluency of speech. The successful speech performance, in turn, enhances the positive emotional reaction. We have all had similar experiences. When we feel confident we are fluent and coordinated—not only in speech but in any motor act, such as holding a cup and saucer at a buffet, deftly hitting a drop shot in tennis, or placing a running bunt in baseball. Apparently, people perform best when the stimulus circumstances elicit positive emotion.

Of course, not all of the stimuli people experience in their daily lives have been emotionally conditioned. Some have been classically conditioned, but in a way that results in only a minimal emotional response. For the most part, then, the speech of both stutterers and nonstutterers is neither facilitated nor disorganized by their reaction to environmental stimuli. In this way the stutterer and the nonstutterer are no different. Like the nonstutterer, the stutterer reacts without great emotion to most of the vast stimulus world that surrounds him, to the words he uses and many of the situations in which he speaks. It should be no surprise, then, that the average stutterer's speech is far more fluent than dysfluent. It is not the absence of fluency, therefore, that sets the stutterer apart from other speakers. It may not even be the quantity of fluency failure that distinguishes a stutterer from a nonstutterer. What seems to set the stutterer apart is that his fluency failures are generally associated with originally neutral situations and words that have been conditioned to elicit negative emotion. Stuttering, then, is the disruption of normal fluency that occurs when specific situations and words (conditioned stimuli) consistently elicit negative emotion (conditioned response). The emotional response elicited by these stimuli interferes with the accurate motor performance that is required for fluent speech, and speech becomes disorganized.

Instrumental Conditioning

Conditioned and unconditioned responses are involuntary, reflexive reactions to stimuli. There are also voluntary responses—ways of adjusting with purpose and direction to environmental stimulation. These adjustive responses are learned from past consequences. For example, certain responses, to certain people, in certain situations, are likely to result in negative or positive stimulation. From experience, we learn to discriminate which adjustive responses will avoid negative consequences and which will bring about positive consequences. In other words, we learn to make those responses that are *instrumental* in reducing negative stimulation or in increasing positive stimulation.

We learn not only *which* response to use, but we learn *when* to use it. We learn which response to use by instrumental conditioning, but we learn when to use it by classical conditioning. Consequently, in the learning of instrumental responses, both classical and instrumental conditioning are involved. Through classical conditioning we learn which situations will result in positive consequences and which situations will result in negative consequences; and through instrumental conditioning we learn which responses to use in order to achieve or avoid the consequences in any given situation. The very same stimulus that is the consequence of a response in instrumental conditioning is also the consequence of the stimulus situation in which it occurred, and when a stimulus is a consequence of another stimulus, we have the arrangement for classical conditioning. The two types of conditioning are practically inseparable. It might be said that this relationship between the two types of conditioning is as follows: We are emotionally motivated by classical conditioning to respond in ways that are instrumental in achieving positive stimulus consequences or in avoiding negative stimulus consequences.

We engage in instrumental responding when we try to get an invitation to an event that we expect to be interesting or pleasant or when we slow down at the sight of a police car. Stutterers do the same thing, trying to please their friends and attain their goals. But in addition, they may attend certain events or become friendly with certain people because there is a better chance of their speaking fluently. In the same way, stutterers may come to feel positively about certain words or phrases. They may be motivated to use them, even if they are not entirely appropriate because they have been

40

associated with fluency and the ability to communicate. The stutterer learns, then, approach responses as well as avoidance responses on the basis of their consequent stimulation.

Since the conditioning histories of stutterers are not exactly alike they will avoid different situations, listeners, and words. There are stutterers who avoid speaking before any group and stutterers who approach such speech situations with eagerness and fluency. Similarly, there are stutterers who are fluent on words that begin with particular vowels or consonants and there are also those who react negatively to the very same sounds and who consistently stutter on them. The commonality among stutterers, then, is not in the particular situations, listeners, or words, to which they react emotionally or in the way that they may approach or avoid these negative stimuli. What stutterers *do* have in common is their negative emotional response to speech-associated stimuli such as these.

Stutterers, like anyone else, will approach stimuli they regard as positive and avoid those they regard as negative. Sometimes negative stimulation is avoided only for an instant, but that is all it takes to *reinforce* a response. On the basis of such momentary reinforcements stutterers can learn to inhale deeply before speaking a feared word, to tap their foot rhythmically while speaking, or to look away from listeners. But these responses are not always successful or instrumental in avoiding negative consequences. Stuttering often occurs anyway, and communication is interfered with or blocked. The stutterer wants to escape from this negative circumstance; he wants to complete the sound or word on which he is blocked by repetition or prolongation. He struggles, adjusts, and varies his responses in an attempt to escape from this negative state of affairs. He may try a great many responses in order to escape; he may, for example, hold his breath, close his eyes, turn his head, swing his arm, stamp his foot, or tighten up his abdominal muscles. Eventually, the fluency failure will end, the sound or word will be completed, and the responses associated with this escape from negative stimulation will be instrumentally conditioned. This reinforcing experience will shape the way he responds. As a result of this experience, he will be more likely to respond in this or in a similar way the next time he tries to escape from negative stimulation. Through repeated experiences he learns a number of different ways of removing negative stimulation. Sometimes he will use one way and sometimes another. Sometimes he will use a combination or sequence of instrumental responses to escape from the negative stimulation that is associated with stuttering. In any event, the stutterer learns, as we all do, to adjust to the environment and the stimulation that emanates from it. The stutterer's instrumental responses, then, are fundamentally like those of the nonstutterer. They differ only in that they are tied specifically to speech and the act of speaking by conditioned negative emotion.

BEHAVIOR THERAPY

From our discussion, we have learned that man reacts both emotionally and adjustively as a result of his individual experiences with his environment. Unfortunately, emotional and adjustive learning are not always adaptive. Some people are afraid of all cars because they were once in an automobile accident. Some people refuse to try to sew, make potato salad, or play bridge because their early attempts were met with strong and consistent negative stimulation. The stutterer is no different. The mere sight of a telephone, an /s/ word, or an audience may send chills through him. Because of his past experiences, he may pretend that he does not know the answer to a teacher's question or that he is severely hard of hearing. In order to avoid or escape negative stimulation he may also have learned to swing his arm, change words, tap his foot, or do any of the things that have been described as secondary symptoms, devices, or associated responses.

How can we modify responses that are inappropriate or maladaptive? We can make these changes by using procedures that alter the stutterer's experience with contingent stimuli. We can provide him with experiences in which he can learn that there is no need to fear the telephone, /s/ words, or specific listeners. We can give him experiences which tell him that these stimuli do not signal the occurrence of negative consequences. Indeed, these experiences can teach him to react positively to speech and the act of speaking. In these ways we can recondition the stutterer so that his classically conditioned emotional responses are more appropriate to the world around him. As far as the instrumental responses are concerned, we can also modify them by manipulating the stimulus consequences of their occurrence. In addition to eliminating these maladaptive avoidance and escape responses, we can shape the stutterer's speech behavior generally in ways that increase the accuracy and acceptability of his speech signals. Behavior modification is therefore not limited to changing maladaptive responses. It includes also the strengthening of appropriate responses already in the stutterer's repertoire.

CLASSICAL CONDITIONING: MODIFICATION PROCEDURES

There are two basic procedures for modifying classically conditioned responses—deconditioning and counterconditioning. Both of these procedures alter the contingent relationship between the conditioned stimulus and the unconditioned stimulus.

Deconditioning

The purpose of deconditioning is to return the conditioned stimulus to its originally neutral status, so that it no longer signals

42

the occurrence of negative stimulation. To accomplish this change, the stutterer must repeatedly experience the conditioned stimulus to which he has come to respond inappropriately. He must do this under conditions that do not permit him to avoid or escape, so that he can find out that the telephone, a specific listener, /s/ words, etc., are not followed by negative stimulation. This is vital. For when a conditioned stimulus is presented repeatedly and in quick succession in the absence of negative consequences it loses its value as a signal of forthcoming danger, and eventually it will fail to arouse the organism. Since there is no longer a consistent relationship between the conditioned and unconditioned stimuli, the classically conditioned relationship between the two stimuli is deconditioned or unlearned. The previously threatening situations, listeners, and words no longer concern the stutterer. He stops being afraid of them because they no longer signal the approach of unpleasant consequences.

Deconditioning can be carried out in many different ways, but the underlying principle is always the same—the conditioned stimulus is no longer contingently followed by the unconditioned stimulus. Speech pathologists have traditionally used this principle to remove the negative emotions of stutterers. They have sent stutterers out to experience those life situations that threaten them but are not objectively dangerous. Stutterers who were frightened by the sight of an audience, who shuddered when a salesgirl approached them, or who dreaded the sound of the phone ringing have been deconditioned when clinicians made arrangements for them to experience these stimuli in the absence of negative consequences. Usually, the stutterers learned from these reality-testing experiences that the stimuli that frightened them were not necessarily followed by or even frequently associated with negative consequences, that the audiences were often polite, that salesgirls can be helpful and friendly, and that a ringing phone is not inherently dangerous.

There are, of course, limits to how useful and efficient such life situation procedures are for deconditoning stutterers. Such procedures *can* lead to behavior change, but they are not always possible to arrange nor are they always therapeutic. Social clubs soon tire of listening to stutterers. A stutterer's first experience with a salesgirl might well be negative, so that conditioning rather than deconditioning might occur. Some experiences are simply impossible to arrange. For these and other reasons, life situation procedures have either been replaced or supplemented by procedures that can be efficiently programmed in a clinical setting. Situations, listeners, words—experiences of various kinds—are tape recorded, put on slides, or filmed so that they can be repeatedly faced in the absence of negative consequences. These reproductions can either be prepared in advance, so that the clinic has a ready library of commonly feared sounds, words, and situations, or the therapist can record specific stimuli that evoke negative emotional responses in their clients. In either case, these stimuli are presented over and over until they become commonplace, unimportant, and no longer threatening for the stutterer. Because of its repeated presentation in the absence of negative consequences, the stimulus no longer makes the stutterer uneasy. When this point is reached he finds that he can stop the presentation and say the sound or word that previously threatened him. Indeed, he can now record his own fluent production and listen to it over and over again. These experiences are helpful not only in deconditioning the stutterer to fear-inducing stimuli but in maintaining the behavior change. The repeated experience of a sound or word in the absence of negative consequences will outweigh the occasional and random negative experiences of life. Thus, deconditioning can be maintained even if random or noncontingent negative experiences do occasionally occur.

Deconditioning experiences do not require the constant presence of a therapist or even a clinical setting. They can be provided also in a listening laboratory to which stutterers can go at a time that is convenient for them. Thus, at any time of the day it should be possible for them to select the appropriate tapes and listen repeatedly to their feared sounds or words until they become neutral stimuli. This laboratory setting can also be used by the therapist to supervise the practice of a group of stutterers. But practice of this kind need not be limited to a laboratory. Deconditioning can take place at home, on the way to work, or at the office. The readily available and inexpensive cassette tape recorders allow deconditioning to be carried out almost anywhere. Furthermore, the success of the deconditioning procedures can then be tested in the reality of these very same settings.

Deconditioning experiences need not be limited to word and sound fears nor to auditory procedures of presentation. Narrative descriptions of stimulus situations that elicit unobjective negative emotion have been tape recorded so that the stutterer can experience them repeatedly in the absence of negative consequences. Stimuli that evoke negative emotion have also been presented visually. Letters, words, people, and places have been repeatedly presented with a slide projector. Videotapes and film clips have been used to present more dynamic stimulus events. Although the equipment is more expensive, the advantages over a tape recorder or a slide projector are obvious. Anyone who has laughed, cried, or been frightened during a movie knows how real the reaction to motion pictures is. And anyone who has heard a joke lose its ability to provoke laughter when repeatedly told should understand why the repeated presentation of feared stimuli reduces the fear they evoke. To bring about fear deconditioning, videotapes and film clips of common experiences are being used more and more. They simplify the procedure through which the history of conditioned stimuli can be modified from those that signal negative consequences to those that are relatively neutral.

Counterconditioning

Counterconditioning is another procedure for modifying a classically conditioned response to a conditioned stimulus. It differs from deconditioning in that a new response is learned. In counterconditioning, the conditioned stimulus, instead of returning to a neutral status, is conditioned to evoke a new conditioned response as a substitute for the old one. So, counterconditioning involves both the *unlearning* of the old response and the *learning* of a new response to replace it. With stutterers, this procedure is used to replace a negative emotional response with a positive emotional response to the same stimulus. The evocation of a particular conditioned response depends upon a specific relationship between a conditioned and an unconditioned stimulus. If this relationship is changed, the conditioned response will also change. Consequently, when a conditioned stimulus, like a word or situation, is followed by a positive consequence rather than a negative one, the conditioned response will be changed as well as the contingency. The conditioned stimulus remains the same, the response is changed.

The events of real life are more likely to compete with counterconditioning than this simplified description would suggest. The negative consequences of conditioned stimuli are often not completely absent. Unconditioned stimulation can be an occasional consequence of the situations and words a stutterer faces. Furthermore, a negative emotional reaction to conditioned stimuli can be maintained even though the negative consequences occur only rarely. Because of this, a newly conditioned relationship between stimuli will be in competition with an older and more established one. Whether a conditioned stimulus will evoke a negative or positive emotional reaction depends, then, on which contingent relationship is the more strongly habituated. The therapist's job is to strengthen the new relationship as much as possible through counterconditioning. It can be strengthened until the words and situations are far more likely to evoke positive than negative reactions.

Although counterconditioning is a viable procedure, it is not a miraculous technique. It requires a workmanlike precision. It depends on clinical steps that are often undramatic and laborious and which are highly specific to the individual in therapy. Before counterconditioning begins, the therapist determines: (1) the conditioned stimuli that elicit an unobjective emotional reaction, (2) the way these various stimuli cluster together to form different categories that elicit negative emotion (for example, telephones, girls, specific word classes, parents, teachers, strangers, or audiences), (3) the relative intensity of the emotional reaction to the different conditioned stimuli that make up a category (for example, there may be a mild reaction to telephoning a buddy, a measurably greater one to calling a girl friend, and a strong reaction to talking to a long-distance operator or an employer), and (4) the frequency with which the stutterer would meet each of the categories of emotion-inducing stimuli if he were not to avoid them. In other words, the speech pathologist must determine the conditioned stimuli that are critical to a stutterer, measure and evaluate the intensity of the emotional reaction they elicit, and find out how important behavior change will be to the patient, at least in terms of the frequency with which he is likely to experience the stimuli that evoke negative emotion.

Determinations of the kind we have been discussing are not difficult or beyond the training level of speech therapists. The behavioral terms used may be a bit unfamiliar, but speech therapists have long recognized the need to determine the situational and word stimuli that arouse a stutterer and disrupt his fluency, the severity of the emotional reaction to specific stimuli, and the frequency with which the stimuli occur. Speech therapists have known too, that these determinations must be based on data; clinical judgments are vital, but hard data about a stutterer's performance are an inestimable aid to the therapist.

An orderly procedure is essential for successful counter-conditioning. The conditioned stimuli within an emotion-evoking category as well as the categories themselves should be presented so that the least feared stimuli are experienced first and the rest in order of the negative emotional reaction they are known to evoke. The categories and stimuli that evoke little negative emotion are presented early. Those that are reacted to more strongly are presented later. This data-bound ordering of the stimuli makes it possible to reduce markedly or even eliminate the therapy drop-out that tends to result when clients are asked to face stimuli that are more threatening than they can withstand. The presentation of conditioned stimuli is ordered also because even a small change in the stutterer's everyday responses will help motivate him to continue therapy and to take the steps that successful behavior modification requires.

Once the order of presentation has been determined, the therapist must decide how to present them for counterconditioning. The conditioned stimuli can be presented auditorally, visually, or audiovisually by means of tape recorders, slide projectors, and film clips or video tapes. They can also be presented through imagination, which may or may not be made more vivid with hypnosis. In any event, for counterconditioning to occur, they must be contingently associated with stimulation that is positive or predominantly positive. In this way the conditioned stimuli will come to evoke a positive rather than a negative emotional response. For this reason, the conditioned stimuli are best presented in a setting that has a positive past history and in which positive stimulation can be contingently delivered. For example, a child who is afraid of all dogs because he was once bitten by one will be faced with this fear-evoking stimulus or a weakened version of it (the word *dog*, a still picture, a cute-looking puppy, or a dog seen at a distance) and then receive stimulation that is known to be pleasant to him. After the conditioned stimulus *dog*, or a version of it, is repeatedly followed by an ice cream cone, playing a favorite game, hitting a punching bag, or whatever the child enjoys, it will no longer evoke fear. This is not to say that in the process of counterconditioning the child will not experience some fear reactions. But if the counterconditioning procedure is designed well, the stimulation that follows *dog* will be more positive than negative. As a result, the *net* emotional reaction will be positive. This dominance of positive consequences over negative must be maintained as the dog is brought closer to the child, in an ordered way. In time, because of the counterconditioning that takes place at each step, the dog's presence will signal positive rather than negative consequences. The child will have learned a new relationship in which the conditioned stimulus *dog* signals that positive unconditioned stimulation is likely to follow. Under such circumstances the conditioned emotional reaction is appropriately positive.

The process of counterconditioning is the same for both children and adults. It applies equally to the stutterer's fear of words, telephones, or people, or to anyone's fear of dogs, cars, or bugs. To be sure, the procedure has to be adjusted for the age of the client and the nature of the problem and for any number of other individual differences. There are, however, certain constants around which the therapeutic strategy must be designed. The therapist must determine the critical conditioned stimuli, group them into categories in terms of their thematic similarity, arrange the component stimuli and the categories themselves in an order that is determined by the intensity of the fear reaction they evoke, and present them in order, beginning with those that are least feared, in a clinical setting where the consequences, the contingent stimuli, are positive.

INSTRUMENTAL CONDITIONING: MODIFICATION PROCEDURES

Although deconditioning and counterconditioning will modify speech-associated fear and therefore the involuntary repetitions and prolongations it precipitates, it may not immediately cause any change in the instrumental adjustive responses. Certainly, if negative emotion has been modified so that stuttering has decreased, there are no longer any negative consequences to escape or avoid.

47

Consequently, instrumental responses will occur less often. Nevertheless, some of them may hang on anyway because they have been conditioned to various stimulus compounds or because they have a complex record of reinforcement spanning a number of years.

The instrumental responses stutterers use are not always successful in permitting them to escape or avoid negative stimulation. Consequently, these responses are only reinforced some of the time. Contrary to what you might think, instrumental responses that have been learned by partial reinforcement are more difficult to extinguish than ones that have been reinforced every time they occurred. Also, many of these responses have come to have reinforcing consequences other than the reduction of negative emotion. They may have been conditioned originally because they permitted the stutterer to avoid or escape negative stimulation, but they can be maintained by positive stimulation. The stutterer's parents may pay more attention to him or to his requests when he closes his eyes and inhales before he speaks. His teachers may tell him that his good grade on an oral report or speech is partly a reward for his perseverance in the face of great difficulty. It is for reasons such as these that a stutterer's instrumental responses may not be immediately or totally eliminated when negative emotional reactions to situations or words are modified. A reduction in negative emotion will usually make them occur less often, but they will continue as long as they are instrumental in attaining positive stimulation.

Because classical and instrumental conditioning are not independent of one another the therapist should plan carefully the behavior therapy for changing these two types of responses. First, the speech therapist must consider that listeners may negatively stimulate the instrumental responses of stutterers and that this very same stimulation can create emotional conditioning. Because listener reactions can reinstate the speech-associated emotion that the therapist has worked so hard to remove, it is extremely important to integrate the therapy for instrumentally and classically conditioned responses. It is for this reason that in two-factor therapy we do not work first just on the negative emotional responses and then just on the maladaptive adjustive responses. Instead, we integrate the modification of emotional responses to specific situations or words with the modification of the instrumental responses that are associated with these very same stimuli. Second, speech therapists must choose carefully from among a number of procedures for modifying instrumental responses. These procedures differ both in their efficiency and in their effect. You will recall that instrumental responses are learned because of the positive consequences of their performance, either an increase in positive stimulation or a decrease in negative stimulation. When such consequences no longer follow an instrumental response, it occurs less and less often. It may also be made to occur less often if it is followed by negative stimulus consequences. The speech therapist therefore has a choice of a number of different methods he can use, singly or in combination, in order to bring about behavior change. He can modify responses through reinforcement, nonreinforcement, and punishment.

Reinforcement

If the consequence of a specific response is positive, the stutterer is informed of its usefulness and will use it more often. The therapist should recognize this relationship so that he can reinforce those speech behaviors that are adaptive. Speech is after all an instrumental response, and much of what the stutterer does when he speaks is adaptive rather than maladaptive. The adaptive speech responses, particularly those that occur infrequently, should be identified and strengthened by positive consequences. Behavior therapy for the stutterer is not, then, simply a matter of making maladaptive responses occur less often. It also includes procedures that make the adaptive ones occur more often. Consequently, the therapist must know the dimensions of adequate speech. He must be able to survey the stutterer's speech responses and tease out those that are relatively adaptive. The performance of these behaviors can then be shaped by the selective use of reinforcement. For example, the therapist can make reinforcement contingent on articulatory accuracy, adequate voice intensity, and an appropriate rate of speaking. Listeners will not then ask the stutterer to repeat what may well have been said fluently just because it was spoken inarticulately, rapidly, or too softly. The therapist may also find it useful to reinforce the at-rest position of the articulators prior to speech, the manner in which speech is initiated, or the rhythm pattern of speech.

Positive consequences can be made contingent on the absence of maladaptive responses as well as on the presence of adaptive ones. You can teach the stutterer what *not* to do as well as what to do. Consequently, the therapist can provide reinforcement when an eye-blink, a lip-purse, or rhythmic foot-tap does not occur. The stutterer will be informed that reinforcement is contingent upon the absence of these behaviors; he learns also that the reinforcement follows a different way of responding. As a result of this information his behavior will be modified so as to bring about more positive consequences.

It is inefficient to wait for the stutterer to discover that when he responds in one way or another he will be rewarded by the therapist. The point of therapy is not to determine the client's intelligence. The stutterer should be told just what responses are going to be reinforced at the beginning. This will quicken the pace of behavior change. Indeed, the stutterer can be told that certain responses will be instrumental in developing a more adequate speech

49

performance—one that is likely to be reinforced and accepted rather than rejected by listeners.

We have been stressing the fact that instructions can increase the efficiency with which the instrumental responses of stutterers are modified. These instructions are not response contingent, they are stimulus contingent. In clinical and real-life settings stutterers can be informed that positive stimulation will follow specific responses that have not yet been made. Through classical conditioning (stimulus-contingent stimulation), then, stutterers can learn to discriminate the responses that will be instrumental in obtaining reinforcement. They need not wait for the instrumental response and its contingent stimulation. Indeed, the instruction will serve as a conditioned stimulus for instrumental responding. This points up again the clinically important interaction between classical and instrumental conditioning.

Nonreinforcement

One of the techniques of nonreinforcement is selective reinforcement. When a therapist selectively reinforces certain responses, he is selectively extinguishing others. If the therapist praises the stutterer for articulating more accurately or talking more loudly, he is at the same time withholding reinforcement from speech that is misarticulated or weakly delivered. Similarly, when the therapist reinforces the stutterer for speaking without blinking his eyes or pursing his lips, reinforcement is being withheld from these maladaptive responses.

In addition to selective reinforcement, the therapist can arrange the speech circumstances so that reinforcement does *not* follow as the consequence of a particular response. If an instrumentally conditioned response occurs repeatedly without reinforcement, the stutterer will come to perform it less and less often. When blinking the eyes, pursing the lips, or changing words are no longer instrumental in bringing about reinforcement, the stutterer will stop using them. The absence of reinforcement informs the stutterer that these responses are not useful.

Of course, the therapist does not have to wait until the stutterer learns that an instrumental response is no longer followed by reinforcement. Behavior modification can be made much more efficient if the therapist informs him that a specific response will not be reinforced, informs him also each time that response is made, and then gives him a great deal of such experience. When using nonreinforcement, the therapist should make the stutterer immediately aware each time the unwanted response occurs. Unless he is consistently and immediately informed, the unwanted behavior will not be modified efficiently. Telling your client to watch himself in a mirror or listen to a recording of his speech is not enough. These procedures are too vague. They do not tell the stutterer explicitly which response is to be changed. In the absence of this specificity the therapist may well be providing noncontingent stimulation rather than stimulation that is contingent on a specific behavior. Noncontingent stimulation is inconsistent—it brings attention to many different behaviors and information about none. In part, such inconsistent stimulation is a result of a definition of stuttering that lacks specificity. Traditionally, stuttering has been described in all inclusive terms, such as "moments of stuttering," so that the absence of reinforcement could be a consequence of anything—a lip-purse, an /s/ -prolongation, a phrase repetition, or a word-change. The inconsistency that results does not serve therapy, it interferes with it.

We may have dealt with stutterers inconsistently because we were concerned that calling attention to "stuttering" would be punishing, that it would increase fear conditioning and consequently increase maladaptive emotional and adjustive responding. This is a very real worry and one that therapists have faced repeatedly. But response-contingent stimulation need not be punishing. Contingent stimuli that are relatively neutral can be informing without being punishing. Any stimulus that the stutterer can discriminate can be used to inform him that a maladaptive response has occurred. A signal light, the word "now," or a tone are examples. Again, the therapist should not wait for awareness to develop. He should call the stutterer's attention to a specific instrumental adjustment and tell him whenever this behavior takes place. Indeed, the therapist should train him to identify accurately the behavior being modified. At first he will make mistakes, but as the target behavior is more precisely identified, the stutterer's awareness will be increased even more than if the therapist continues to apply the contingent reaction.

The speed with which behavior change occurs under nonreinforcement depends partly on the frequency of this experience. The more often the response occurs without reinforcement, the more quickly it will be extinguished. As a result, when the response occurs, the stutterer should make a precisely imitative version of it repeatedly. Through this massed repetition the stutterer experiences an increased number of unreinforced occurrences of the maladaptive response. The massed practice also serves to increase the stutterer's awareness of the unreinforced response; he learns its "feel," and this serves as an informing stimulus that carries over to settings and times outside the clinic.

Massing a nonreinforced response serves another purpose too. When a response is made repeatedly in quick succession, its occurrence can be temporarily inhibited. Thus, if a stutterer repeatedly swings his arm, turns his head, or purses his lips, the response becomes increasingly difficult to make. The time interval between occurrences of the response will become longer and longer.

As the same response is repeated over and over again, there will develop what has been called response "fatigue" or reactive inhibition, as a result of which the response is temporarily suppressed. The time period during which this response is not made eventually becomes long enough so that the temporary inability to make the response can be used to produce a conditioned inhibition that has clinical significance. Significant conditioned inhibition will result if, during the rest period when the stutterer is unable to make the instrumental response, the therapist presents a stimulus that previously led to its occurrence. With this technique, the *inability* to make the maladaptive response can be conditioned to stimulus events such as ordering in a restaurant, talking on the phone, or speaking in class. In other words, response inhibition can be conditioned so that events which previously elicited it will now keep it from occurring. Conditioned inhibition of a stimulus-response relationship is not temporary; it does not dissipate with rest like reactive inhibition does. The stimuli presented when the instrumental response cannot be made come to serve as conditioned or learned inhibitors of its occurrence. This is not to say that the response will not occur in other settings. The conditioned inhibition of an instrumental adjustive response is specific to the stimulus scenes that are presented and to those that are like them. The response will continue to occur in other settings unless these too are made to serve as conditioned inhibitors.

There are then a number of techniques of nonreinforcement that a therapist can use. None of them needs to be used alone. Often, in fact, the most efficient strategy is for the therapist to use a combination of these techniques to modify an adjustive response. The fundamental principle behind these various techniques is nonreinforcement.

Punishment*

There is much disagreement about the term punishment and it is used by different people in quite different ways. Therefore, it is important that we know what a therapist means when he says that he uses punishment to modify stuttering. What exactly does he *do?*

Punishment may be said to take place when a specified response is consistently followed by a negative stimulus. The negative stimulus need not occur every time the behavior occurs, it may be delivered every fifth or tenth time. It does not even have to be delivered immediately, as long as it is a consequence of the response. The response must be specified. It is not very helpful to say that a negative stimulus is contingent on "stuttering moments" or "secondary behaviors." This is too vague. Stuttering moments include various behaviors. To discuss the effect of punishment

---

*The comments made in this section are based, in part on experiments which are listed at the end of this chapter.

meaningfully, it is necessary to specify the behavior that is contingently followed by a negative stimulus.

Punishment, like reinforcement or nonreinforcement, is informative. When a stutterer receives an electric shock or a verbal reprimand as a consequence of a response, he soon becomes aware of the contingent relationship. He may then suppress the response. Despite the fact that behavior change may result, the therapist might be best advised to consider other, less risky, techniques for achieving the same end. Behavior can often be modified at least as efficiently with nonreinforcement and selective reinforcement procedures. Moreover, nonpunishing approaches to behavior modification appear to be more lasting and less likely to have nontherapeutic side effects than punishment. Punishment is not being rejected here for moral reasons (except insofar as risking harm to a client is immoral). If punishment could lead to normal fluency it would be inhumane to withhold it from stutterers. It is being rejected because its use involves a risk that is not commensurate with its limited effectiveness. One of the reasons punishment is risky and other procedures for modifying behavior are preferred is that it cannot be made critically specific to a particular response. The therapist cannot guarantee that the punishing stimulus will be contingent on only a maladaptive response. If the therapist punishes a stutterer for pursing his lips he may also be punishing him for all the other behaviors that are present at the same time. If all of these concomitant behaviors happened to be instrumentally conditioned responses that were maladaptive and that had a similar learning history, the result would probably be beneficial. The punishment would probably lead to the suppression of a number of maladaptive responses. The fact that complex moments of stuttering have occasionally been reduced by punishment may be evidence for this multiple effect. But such an effect is not the only possible one or even the most likely one. The responses that occur at about the same time as the target response may well have learning histories that are different. Punishment does not suppress all responses—there are some that it increases. An increase would not be unanticipated for example if the response being punished had been learned as an adjustment to punishing stimulation. It is noteworthy, in this respect, that many of the responses of stutterers seem to have this history. Another reason for concern is that a negative stimulus that is contingent on one response may also be noncontingent as far as other behaviors are concerned. This is important because noncontingent negative stimulation has been observed to cause certain stuttering behaviors to occur more often. Critical also is the evidence that noncontingent negative stimulation leads not only to an increase in fluency failures but to fluency failures that resist behavior change. The use of punishment is contraindicated for still another reason. The suppressive effect of contingent negative stimulation is most noticeable with instrumental responses. In contrast, it seems to increase the frequency and the magnitude of emotional responding. But even if the therapist were not concerned with the emotional aspects of a stutterer's difficulty—even if he were concerned only with the speech disruptions—he should know that punishment has not led to any significant decrease in repetitions. The repetitions of stutterers have at best been minimally reduced for short periods of time and at worst increased markedly by punishment. Punishment is not, then, a procedure that is applicable to all behaviors. It is apparently not a powerful tool for modifying the repetitions of stuttering and it may well do harm.

There is more to be considered. Punishment has been known to have undesirable side effects. It has increased the frequency of repetitions, prolongations, and maladaptive adjustments. Punishment has not only had undesirable effects on the contingently stimulated behavior, it also has had undesirable effects on the noncontingently stimulated behaviors that occur at the same time; they have been increased rather than decreased. The lack of a decrease has not been the result of using a punishing stimulus that was too weak. On the contrary, a mildly punishing stimulus seems more likely to decrease contingently stimulated repetitions and less likely to increase noncontingently stimulated repetitions than a strong punisher. That a strong punisher leads to more stuttering repetitions than a mild one is not totally surprising. After all, a mild punisher is less disruptive than one that is very strong. A strong punisher can set off an intense emotional reaction, and this reaction can interfere with normal fluency. At least as much change in instrumental responding has occurred when the contingent stimulus was relatively neutral. What seems necessary is that the stutterer be informed of the occurrence of a maladaptive adjustment. Any stimulus that can be discriminated will serve this purpose. Punishing stimuli need not be used.

Summing up and Looking Ahead

We have stressed that all responses are not learned in the same way and that the therapist must bear this in mind as he sets about to modify a stutterer's behavior. Consequently, we have focussed our attention on both classical and instrumental conditioning. It may be considered unfortunate that the two-factor approach does not give the therapist one tool that he can use with all behaviors, but by distinguishing between the two types of responses, the two-factor approach provides a more efficient strategy for behavior change. The probability of successfully modifying behavior is much less when we treat all responses as if they were learned the same way. But just because we have distinguished between classically and instrumentally conditioned responses does not mean that the two types are unrelated. We have pointed out their interrelationship and stressed its clinical significance.

Although the two-factor approach has the great advantage of additional efficiency as a result of not oversimplifying stuttering and associated instrumental behavior, it has a disadvantage in not being able to supply any direct technique for modifying classically conditioned responses. Someday, however, this may be possible, and the possibility has great clinical significance. Consequently, we must maintain the more comprehensive two-factor approach and make precise observations and measurements of classically conditioned responses. The measurement of emotional responses may not be as easy as the measurement of instrumental responses, but it is not impossible, even now. Heart rate, palmar sweating, muscular tension, and breathing rate are just a few of the reactions we can currently observe and reliably measure. Technological advancements, like those that led to the current surge of interest in instrumental responding, are sure to increase the attention given to classically conditioned responses. Eventually, we will learn more about the part conditioned emotion plays in disturbing speech and in motivating instrumental adjustments. This technology will also give the speech therapist a much better way of measuring the effectiveness of his therapeutic techniques. He will be able to monitor the effect of his stimulus-contingent as well as his response-contingent procedures for changing the emotional and adjustive responses of stutterers. But we must begin *now* to observe these response classes if we are to learn more about them.

Finally, we have seen that there are a number of issues surrounding therapy for stutterers. These issues have not been fully resolved. Many areas of disagreement remain because behavior theory and therapy is in its infancy. We have not yet arrived at *the way* that is the most efficient for modifying all behaviors. The therapist is best advised, therefore, to remain flexible so that he can change as new information comes out of the laboratory and clinic.

Bibliography

Brookshire, R.H., "Effects of Random and Response Contingent Noise upon Disfluencies of Normal Speakers." *Journal of Speech and Hearing Research,* 1969, pp. 126-134.

Brookshire, R.H., and Eveslage, R. E., "Verbal Punishment of Disfluency by Random Delivery of Aversive Stimuli." *Journal of Speech and Hearing Research,* 1969, pp. 383-388.

Frederick, C.J., III, "An Investigation of Learning Theory and Reinforcement as Related to Stuttering Behavior." Unpublished doctoral dissertation, University of California at Los Angeles, 1955.

Martin, R.R., Brookshire, R.H., and Siegel, G. M., "The Effects of Response Contingent Punishment on Various Behaviors Emitted During a 'Moment of Suttering.' " Unpublished manuscript, University of Minnesota, 1964.

Starkweather, C. W., "The Simple, Main, and Interactive Effects of Contingent and Noncontingent Shock of High and Low Intensity on Stuttering Repetitions." Unpublished doctoral dissertation, Southern Illinois University, 1969.

Rescorla, R. A., "Pavlovian Conditioning and its Proper Control Procedures." *Psychology Review*, 1967, pp. 71-80.

Webster, L. M., "An Audio-Visual Exploration of the Stuttering Moment." Unpublished master's thesis, Southern Illinois University, 1966.

Webster, L. M., "A Cinematic Analysis of the Effects of Contingent Stimulation on Stuttering and Associated Behaviors." Unpublished doctoral dissertation, Southern Illinois University, 1968.

Readings

Brutten, E. J., and Shoemaker, D. J., *The Modification of Stuttering.* Englewood Cliffs, N. J.: Prentice-Hall, Inc., 1967.

Beecroft, R. S., *Classical Conditioning.* Goleta, Calif.: Psychonomic Press, 1966.

Kimble, G. A., *Foundations of Conditioning and Learning,* New York: Appleton-Century, 1967.

Kimble, G. A., *Conditioning and Learning.* New York: Appleton-Century, 1961.

Wolpe, J., *Psychotherapy by Reciprocal Inhibition.* Stanford, Calif., Stanford University Press, 1958.

Wolpe, J., *The Practice of Behavior Therapy.* New York: Pergaman Press, 1969.

PART TWO

Example and Analysis

In the preceding section we presented the basic information about the two-factor and operant approaches to stuttering therapy. Although both of these presentations include illustrations in which these conditioning principles are actually applied in treatment, we felt it would be helpful to the practicing clinician if we could at least provide a play-by-play account of an operant program which has been used not only experimentally but therapeutically, and we included the chapter by Dr. Ryan for this purpose. We felt no corresponding need to provide a similar account to illustrate two-factor therapy since this also includes operant conditioning, and its exposition by Dr. Brutten has sufficient examples of therapy techniques for modifying both classically and instrumentally conditioned behaviors.

Besides, we wanted to use the space for a different purpose—one which we felt was a very important one. We hope that this book will cause the practicing clinician to take a good hard look at his own therapy for stuttering in terms of what we know about learning theory. We did not think we could persuade the reader to do this by logical argument or by exhortation. As practicing clinicians ourselves, we have little faith in either of these procedures.

Our solution to the problem turned out to be rather obvious. We decided to provide an example which would show how another therapist scrutinized and described his own unique therapy in terms of learning theory. At first, we considered selecting one of the kinds of stuttering therapy typical of current practice in the United States. Instead (perhaps to lessen our own vulnerability), we asked Dr. Helbert Damsté of the University of Utrecht, The Netherlands, to undertake the same task we hope our readers will attempt—to describe the kind of stuttering therapy he does in learning theory terms, and to state the learning principles which might be involved in the various techniques.

As you will observe, Dr. Damste does not confine his explanations solely to classical or to instrumental conditioning. Though in his commentary he cites both as occurring, he is also concerned with those other processes, both cognitive and physiological, that the learning theorists and operant conditioners rarely deal with. The American reader may be surprised, as we were, to find that many of the therapeutic procedures which he describes can be justified in terms of learning theory. We examined them with real interest (if not complete acceptance) in much the same spirit that he surveyed our own methods, many of which defy rational explanation. If we are ever to evolve a consistently effective treatment for stuttering, all of us must understand why we do what we do.

An Illustration of Operant Conditioning Therapy for Stuttering

BRUCE P. RYAN, Ph. D.

Now you are familiar with the basic theory underlying operant conditioning for stuttering, but you want to know how to plan it and how to begin. This chapter should provide that information by illustrating an operant conditioning therapy program. This program is in three phases: establishment, transfer, and maintenance. In the establishment phase, the goal is to help the person achieve fluent, naturally conversational speech in the presence of the therapist. In the transfer phase, the goal is continued fluent speech but in a wide variety of speaking situations. And in the maintenance phase, the goal is continued fluent speech in a wide variety of settings, but over an extended period of time.

There are many different operant programs for the first phase, that is, for establishing fluent speech. Among them are the use of prolonged speech, punishment in some form or another, and gradually increasing the length and complexity of fluent utterances. We don't yet know which program is best for which person. All of them, however, are accomplished with small steps and appropriate reinforcement. Once any one of these different establishment programs has been used, so that fluent conversational speech has been established in the clinical setting, the transfer and maintenance phases are begun. Figure 1 illustrates the relationship of these phases to each other.

Of the two general aspects of stuttering behavior, speech and feelings, the operant program presented in this chapter will deal only with the former. The speech act, composed of fluent and stuttered words, is overt and measurable, and stuttered speech is the common presenting problem of stutterers—it is why they have sought speech therapy. Feelings, important as they may be, are not easily observed and measured, so that it is difficult to deal with them systematically. Furthermore, we have observed that many of our clients change their feelings and attitudes when they become more fluent. We all know that one's self-concept can change as one becomes better able to perform certain tasks, such as speaking. Should further research demonstrate that it is necessary or desirable to deal directly with feelings and attitudes as well as overt speech responses, then we may do so within the operant system. Several illustrations of such operant programs were given by Shames in the previous chapter.

One of the principles of operant technology is that the clinician must carefully define the behavior that is to be changed. We have

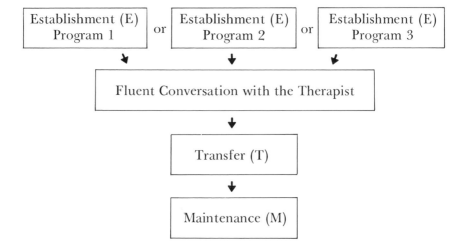

| Establishment (E) Program 1 | or | Establishment (E) Program 2 | or | Establishment (E) Program 3 |

Fluent Conversation with the Therapist

Transfer (T)

Maintenance (M)

Figure 1. Flow Chart of Operant Stuttering Therapy: General

found it convenient to treat the "stuttered word" as a unit of behavior. Usually, these are some form of whole-word repetition, part-word repetition, prolongation, and struggle. The word *struggle* is used here to describe those behaviors that have been called secondary stuttering, such as lip-puckering, tongue-protrusion, etc. We have also restricted our definition to behaviors of the mouth, face, and head only. We realize that this classification system is not perfect, but we have found that the more subtle stuttering behaviors, such as speeding up the rate of speech or circumlocution, are not easily or reliably identified. Also, we have noticed that the need for these behaviors declines as the stutterer becomes more fluent—an observation we have made of most of the behaviors that have traditionally been defined as secondary symptoms. Presumably, the original reason for the acquisition of all of these behaviors was stuttering. We realize, then, that these behaviors exist, but we do not feel that they can be identified easily or reliably enough to be properly counted. Since we cannot count them we do not treat them. We do, however, try to control them to some extent by starting with reading. In this system of definition, both large and small stuttered words receive equal weight, and, gross as this classification is, we have found it adequate for carrying out the programs we use.

The second principle is that the clinician must count carefully how often each of the behaviors he is interested in occurs and keep a record of the count. It is through such careful counting that we measure the frequency with which a behavior occurs. This kind of measurement is boring and time-consuming, but you will be pleased at the result. The information you derive from counting tells you whether or not your program has been adequate, whether or not you are making progress. The procedure is simple—time the person's talking time, count the number of stuttered words, and divide the number of stuttered words by the time spent talking. If a stutterer speaks for five minutes and stutters on ten words, we divide 5 into 10 and arrive at 2 stuttered words per minute. This gives us a smaller number to deal with and permits us to make allowances for different lengths of time spent talking. When a stutterer has very long blocks and a very slow rate of speaking, we also count the total number of words spoken. This gives us a better picture of such a stutterer's behavior. For such a stutterer, an increase in the frequency of stuttering behavior would be a good sign. Fortunately, because total word-counting is very laborious, we don't need to do it very often. In some of the steps in certain programs, we count the number of "correct responses" (for example, identifying a stuttered word) and the number of total responses (the number of stuttered words). From these numbers we can compute a percentage of correctness. If, for example, the stutterer has 10 correct identifications out of 20 total stuttered words, he would have attained 50 per cent accuracy. Counting is crucial to the operant program, in fact, it may be the single most important procedure we use. When a hand counter and an appropriate recording form are used, counting is quite automatic and not as repugnant as you might think.

The third principle is that the clinician must designate before he begins a criterion of proficiency so as to determine when the client can move on to the next step of the program. We have used either a low stuttering rate, commonly 0.5 stuttered words per minute, or a high percentage of correctness, commonly 90 per cent. When a client can speak with either 0.5 stuttered words per minute or less, or when he can perform with 90 per cent accuracy or more, then he is ready to go on to the next step. Certainly, the choice of a criterion measure is somewhat subjective. In fact, we have used 1.0, 0.5, and 0.0 stuttered words per minute as criteria, and we found that 0.5 is best because it allows for a certain amount of therapist or client error but still represents acceptable fluency. We have also used 60-100 per cent accuracy and have found 90 per cent to be a reasonable compromise which allows for some error but not too much. Both of these criteria are used in the illustrated program that follows.

A fourth principle is that the steps within a program must be covered in an appropriate sequence. The sequence must be one which causes the client to have only a few failures. The first step is often simply a count of stuttered words, and the last step is fluent conversational speech in the client's environment. If a breakdown occurs, the client is returned to a previous step where he was successful or put on a "branching step" to give him additional training.

A fifth principle is that the clinician must systematically provide a consequence for the behavior that is to be changed. In the beginning, a great deal of reinforcement is necessary, but later on it is better to reduce the amount. Fluent speech should be positively reinforced. Stuttered words are either ignored or they are pointed out and the client is asked to repeat them. Rewards and punishments may take many forms. Usually, we have used verbal praise for reward, such as "Good," and verbal admonishment for punishment, such as "Say it again." Although verbal rewards and punishments are usually adequate, for unusual problems of motivation, other types of reinforcement can be used, such as points, candy, released time from therapy, etc.

These principles are illustrated in the following description of an operant conditioning program for modifying stuttering behavior. Some of the procedures will be new. Some you have used or heard about before. But the critical point is that the procedures, new or old, be carried out according to the principles we have just described, and in a rigorous, systematic manner.

The program that follows is only one of many. It is, in fact, a composite of several programs that have been used with a number of different stutterers who varied both in age and in the severity of the problem. Its purpose is to teach fluent speaking. There are three phases: establishment, transfer, and maintenance; there are five basic steps: base line, identification, cancellation, prolongation, and fluency; and there are three modes: reading, monologue, and conversation. The relationship of these parts to one another is demonstrated in Figure 2.

The time spent in each session depends on the amount of time the therapist and client have. Ideally contacts should be daily, with a minimum of 20 minutes per session. We have found it best to have a high intensity of contact in the beginning and then fade to a lesser amount later. At the beginning of each session there should be a brief review of the preceding step. This is particularly important when sessions are separated by weekends. For equipment, you need only a stop watch and a hand counter.

The program described here will rarely run less than 6 hours for the establishment phase, 6 hours for the transfer phase, and 20 hours for the maintenance phase, or a total of 32 hours. This time depends on how rapidly the person can complete the steps. Some take longer than others. Our shortest program ran 15 hours, and our longest ran 375 hours over a three year period.

We are now ready to look at the program itself. We have set it up so that there is a description of the program on the left side of the page and a rationale, or explanation, of the program on the right side under the word *commentary*. You will also find an occasional illustration from an actual case.

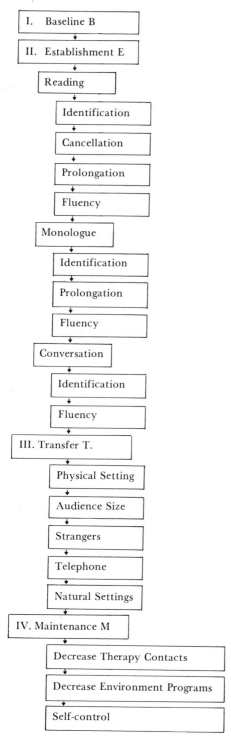

Figure 2. Flow Chart of Operant Stuttering Therapy: Specific

I. Baseline

<table>
<tr><td>

DESCRIPTION

The client reads for twenty minutes, engages in monologue for twenty minutes, and converses for twenty minutes. The therapist counts stuttered words and observes stuttering behavior. These procedures are repeated three times. The therapist times each session and computes stuttered word rate per minute. He may also classify the behaviors into wholeword repetitions, part-word repetitions, etc.

</td><td>

COMMENTARY

This procedure has two purposes: It allows the therapist to observe the stuttering as it occurs in the three modes of reading, monologue, and conversation, and it allows the client to get used to the situation. There are usually differences in the three modes.

</td></tr>
</table>

Illustration No. 1. Stan, a fourteen year old boy, had stuttered for several years. He came to the University Summer Clinic from his home town some 150 miles away. He was bright and motivated. His parents were well educated and extremely interested in his speech problem. His mother, in fact, came and lived with him near the clinic. He had had very little speech therapy before he came to us.

Stan demonstrated a baseline rate of 4 stuttered words per minute in reading and 24 stuttered words per minute in monologue. No baseline measure was taken in conversation because we believed that the monologue sample was enough. His stuttering was composed mostly of part-word repetitions, whole-word repetitions, and exhalations of air preceding words. All of these behaviors occurred at a high rate.

II. Establishment Phase

<table>
<tr><td>

DESCRIPTION

A. Reading.

The client is instructed to read aloud. During each of the following four steps and substeps, the therapist times the client and computes the stuttered word rate per minute.

</td><td>

COMMENTARY

Reading is a good place to start. It allows the therapist to control substitutions and circumlocutions, and at the same time supplies content for the client. Of course, for non-readers, the step has to be omitted, and for poor readers it is difficult. We try to minimize reading errors (by selecting easy material) because a revision in reading is difficult to distinguish from a stuttering

</td></tr>
</table>

repetition. To make the distinction, the therapist must devise a set of rules. For example, "tuck, truck," a phonetic revision, would be considered a reading revision and not a stuttering.

1. Identification
a. The therapist identifies the stuttered word, both visibly and audibly, for the client.

This step is omitted for young children. Omission of this step does not damage the program, although the step is helpful for most people. In order to identify the word, the therapist says "there" or clicks the counter after telling the client that the click will serve as such a signal. The purpose of this step is to teach the client to count his stuttered words accurately, that is, to count the same thing that the therapist is counting. There may be a depression in rate during this step.

b. Out loud, the therapist and the client count stuttered words together.

This gives the client an opportunity to count along with the therapist. The therapist delays his counting slightly and lets the client take the lead.

c. The therapist continues to count, but does so silently, while the client continues to count out loud. Each time the client's identification agrees with the therapist's, the therapist says "good" or gives the client a point. When 90% accuracy has been achieved, the client proceeds to the next step.

Usually, this simple training program is enough to teach the client to count accurately. Later on in the program, his ability to count accurately will enhance his performance. Note that reinforcement is started in this step; it should be given for every correct response (accurate identification) and should follow the response immediately.

2. Cancellation.

The therapist and the client continue to count stuttered words, but the client is instructed also to repeat each stuttered word in a prolonged manner, e.g., "c-cat" is repeated "caaaat" or "c-at." The client may prolong either the vowel or the initial consonant. The therapist models this behavior and has the client practice it 10 times. The therapist says "good" or gives a point for each correct modification. When the client can modify 90% or more of his stuttered words in this way, he goes on to the next step.

The identification process, which was begun in the first step, is continued throughout the program. If the client drops below 90% identification, the therapist takes him back to the identification step. The cancellation step combines identification with cancellation. Cancellation in itself is not critical; it is only a step along the way to fluent speech. There is usually a reduction in the rate of stuttering during this step because the client stops and repeats each stuttered word. Note that the cancellation is not counted as a stuttered word, and the prolongation should be smooth and easy. Reinforcement should be 100%.

3. Prolongation

Both the therapist and the client continue to count stuttered words. The client is further instructed to prolong any word on which he anticipates stuttering. Again, the prolongation may be either on the vowel or on the initial consonant. The therapist models the behavior and has the client practice it 10 times. "Good" or points are again used to reinforce each correct prolongation. When the client is able to modify 90% or more of his stuttered words, he goes on to the next step.

The purpose of this step is to move the prolongation behavior established in the last step back before the stuttered word. This may require several trials. Any remaining cancellation behavior should drop out by the end of this step. In an alternate variation of this program, the therapist starts with this step. This variation speeds up the program but runs the risk of introducing failure into the task. In another variation, the client prolongs every word. This variation is particularly well suited to the client who has difficulty anticipating stuttered words. An improvement in fluency should occur in this step.

4. Fluency

The identification procedures are continued. In addition, the

By the time this step has been reached, stuttering frequency should be greatly decreased, so client is instructed to read as fluently as he can, first one word at a time, then two, then three, and so on. Then one fluent sentence at a time, then two, and so on. After sentences, paragraphs are introduced as units, then pages. The therapist should say "good" or give a point after each substep. When the client has reached the point where he can read five pages fluently, .5 stuttered words per minute or less or 20 minutes of fluent reading, whichever type of measurement is being used, he may go on to the next mode.

that fluent reading is highly probable. Furthermore, success is also more likely because of the decrease in the length of the utterances and the initial increase in reinforcement. The criterion of .5 stuttered words per minute means that there must be no more than 1 stuttered word for every two minutes. In the initial substeps, which are less than two minutes long, the client will have to return to the preceding step every time he stutters. During this step, prolongations should stop, and this is accomplished by counting them as stuttered words. It is possible to use step 4 alone, but there is much risk of failure. The final goal of 5 pages of fluent reading or 20 minutes of fluent reading is somewhat arbitrary. We have found, however, that with less time than this the client does not have enough opportunity to demonstrate his ability, and more time than this is redundant. During this step reinforcement should be given less often than 100% of the time.

The client continues reading at the beginning of each subsequent session. He must read fluently for 2 minutes before he can go on to the next mode. This may take longer than two minutes.

This procedure maintains the fluent reading and sets the stage for fluent monologue.

B. Monologue

The identification process continues. The client is instructed to speak aloud on a topic of his choice. The sessions are timed and the number of stuttered words per minute is

Most people will talk without too much prompting if they have been instructed to talk. For nonreaders, of course, the therapist starts with this mode. For reticent speakers, the therapist may use pictures or computed. Steps 3 and 4 from the reading mode are repeated in monologue. When the client is able to be fluent in monologue for 20 minutes, he may go on to the next mode.

simply suggest topics to stimulate speech. In either case, the therapist should talk as little as possible so as to keep the situation as close to a true monologue as possible. You may begin with step 4 in the monologue situation, but it is usually better to go back to step 3 as a review. Stuttering rate may increase slightly in the monologue mode.

The client continues to read fluently for 2 minutes in the beginning of each session, but now he also must engage in monologue for 2 minutes without stuttering before he can go on to the next mode.

This process sustains the fluent reading and fluent monologue and sets the stage for fluent conversation.

C. Conversation

The identification procedures are continued. The client is instructed to converse about any topic that interests him. The therapist should talk about half of the time or less, and the amount of time the client spends talking is measured and the number of stuttered words per minute computed. Step 4 from the monologue mode is repeated. As soon as the client is able to engage in fluent conversation (0.5 stuttered words per minute or less) for 10 minutes, he may move on to the transfer phase.

Conversation is the most difficult mode. The therapist has to be able to count, compute, reinforce, and carry on a normal conversation. With practice, it can be done. An effort should be made to make the conversation as normal as possible, with either the client or the therapist choosing topics. It is best to avoid a question and answer session, but at the same time you should not hesitate to make statements. It is also advisable to be quiet now and then. The conversation can be built up in complexity by starting with one word utterances and gradually leading into normal conversation. Stuttering rate may increase during this mode.

Illustration No. 2. In Stan's case, the program consisted of having him prolong any word he anticipated stuttering on, having him repeat each word he stuttered on in a prolonged manner, and verbally reinforcing him for fluent speech. In other words, we

68

combined steps 2 and 3 and taught them concurrently. Stan showed an immediate decrease in stuttering rate under these conditions. As criteria we used 1 stuttered word per minute for 20 minutes of reading and 20 minutes of fluent monologue. Stan achieved these goals after 24 hours of instruction. He then moved on to conversation, and, in 6 hours, he was able to speak fluently for 20 minutes in that mode.

III. Transfer Phase

DESCRIPTION

Throughout the transfer phase, the client continues to first read fluently for 2 minutes, then engage in monologue fluently for 2 minutes, then emit 2 minutes of fluent conversation (0.5 stuttered words per minute or less) before moving on to further work.

In most of the following steps, the mode will be conversation, although there will be some monologue in the large groups. The therapist uses the same instructions and procedures as in the last part of step 4 in conversation He instructs the person to speak fluently (0.5 stuttered words per minute) and returns him to the previous step if he goes above this rate.

The identification process is continued.
A. Physical Setting (10 minutes each)
   1. Therapy room with the door open
   2. Immediately outside the therapy room
   3. Down the hall from the therapy room
   4. Outside the building
   5. While walking around outside the building, but away from it

COMMENTARY

This procedure helps to sustain all the work that has preceded.

Some people, especially children, begin to transfer their new fluent speech spontaneously by this time. The therapist should try to measure this transfer by interviewing the client and the people in his environment and by observing him in a number of different settings. Even when transfer has already begun, it is best to go through the whole phase.

This gives the client support as he tries to use his new fluent speech in different settings.

These steps may seem small, and even unnecessary, but they are an important part of the transfer sequence. They make it possible for the client to be successful in transferring his fluent speech to other settings.

6. In different rooms in other buildings where there are other people, for example, a restaurant or school lunch room

B. Audience Size (10 minutes each)
   1. One more person is added to the audience. This person observes but does not take part.
   2. The new person takes part.
   3. Another person joins the group, making 3 in the audience. He does not take part.
   4. The third person takes part.
   5-8. This procedure continues until there are 5 people in the group.
   9. The client gives a speech to an audience of 10 people.
   10. The client gives a speech to an audience of 10 people.
   11. The client gives a speech to an audience of 15 people.

C. Strangers and Physical Setting (5 minutes each)
   1. The client makes a list of speaking situations he commonly encounters (or avoids), in which strangers are involved and speech is required.
   2. The therapist then goes through each of these situations with the client.
   3. The client goes through each of these situations

The purpose of this step is to gradually, systematically increase the number of listeners. These listeners can be strangers, friends, relatives, spouses, teachers, classmates, or even other persons who stutter provided that they, too, are at the same level of fluency. They may be the same people all the way through or they may be new people for each situation. They may also be trained to reinforce fluency and to count stuttered words. Note that it is better to have several short speeches than one 10-minute speech.

Step B can be combined with Step A so that the group interactions take place in different physical settings. Decisions about combining steps, however, should depend on the client's performance and the availability of the audience.

This list will vary with the age of the client and his daily communication activities. Ideally, these should be real situations, but they may have to be contrived. Strangers may have to be prepared for the client, etc. If both types are mixed, it is best to have the contrived situations precede the real ones. The purpose of this activity is to allow the therapist to observe the client. There is

70

alone, reporting to the therapist.

    a. With the therapist present but at some distance

    b. Without the therapist.

no harm in repeating a situation in order to get the information.

The client should do his own counting during these situations. Usually, the situations will require only brief utterances by the client. If he should talk extensively in them, then the time period should be extended so that he must talk to many different strangers.

D. Telephone (Use 5 minutes or 10 calls each)
  1. The client practices calling, answering, and conversing with the therapist but without a phone.
  2. A fake telephone is introduced, and the same activity is continued.
  3. A real phone is introduced.
  4. The same activities are continued, but friends or relatives are substituted for the therapist.
  5. Strangers are substituted for friends and relatives.

Because so many people who stutter have difficulty talking on the phone, a special program is sometimes necessary. Children, unless they use the phone an unusual amount, seem to have less difficulty than adults. Some adults show such extreme fear that extra substeps, such as saying "hello" and hanging up, may be necessary for them to complete the sequence successfully.

Ideally, these should be real phone calls, but they may have to be contrived.

E. Natural Environment (10 minutes each)
  1. School
    a. With the therapist
    b. Without the therapist present, but with the client reporting back to him.
  2. Home
    a. With the therapist
    b. Without the therapist, but with the client reporting back to him
  3. Work
    a. With the therapist

In these settings, the therapist acts more as an observer than as a participant. This is possible partly because some of these situations were touched on earlier when, in the transfer phase, friends and relatives were brought in.

In the school situation, the therapist may train the teacher and class to observe and reinforce the person for fluent speech.

b. Without the therapist, but with the client reporting back to him.

In the home, a parent or spouse may have already been trained in one of the preceding steps.

Work is an important natural environment for the adult. It is often a difficult environment for therapy, but worth the time and effort.

The therapist will want to get feedback about these situations, and to achieve it he asks the client to hand in written reports, including a count of stuttered words, and he asks the client's friends and relatives to report to him.

Illustration No. 4. During the transfer phase, Stan continued to read, engage in monologue, and converse every day. Stan's audience was gradually increased from 2 through 56, and we included his mother toward the end of the phase. We gradually made the conversational setting more complex and included the telephone, strangers, a variety of physical settings, and group discussion. Throughout the transfer phase, which took 42 hours of instruction, Stan continued to stutter on less than one word per minute. During the weekends, Stan's fluency gradually transferred to his home, and his parents reported that he was fluent in all speaking situations.

IV. Maintenance Phase

DESCRIPTION

The three modes, reading, monologue, and conversation, are continued. The therapist, the client, and the people in his environment should continue to evoke and reinforce fluent speech. Gradually, the identification procedure is faded out, and the reinforcements are presented less often, but the client continues to time himself and to count stuttered words.

COMMENTARY

The purpose of the maintenance program is to decrease the number of therapy contacts and activities gradually and systematically until the client is fluent for long periods of time (a year, for example) with only one or two therapy sessions. We know the least about what influences bring about success or failure in this phase. It appears to be very

72

important, however, that the sessions, and thus the reinforcement, occur at varied intervals.

A. Therapy Contacts

The number of therapy contacts is gradually reduced. The reading, monologue, and conversation are repeated at first for 3-5 minutes and then faded to 2 minutes. If the client has been coming in daily, his sessions are changed to 4 times a week, then 3, every two weeks, once a month, once a year. The following steps are also taken:

Any sign of breakdown, such as an increase in stuttering to one word per minute or more, calls for either more therapy contacts or a whole new program. Only if fluency is maintained are the therapy contacts faded out. Reports from friends and relatives help in making this determination.

1. The therapist talks to the client on the phone, first weekly, then monthly, etc.

The therapist and the client should take turns calling each other.

2. The client sends in written reports on his speech, first weekly, then monthly, etc.

These reports and tape recordings should be answered as soon as possible either by letter or by phone.

3. The client sends in tape recordings made in a variety of settings, first weekly, then monthly, etc.

4. The therapist visits the client in his home, first weekly, then monthly, etc.

Just as the client needs reinforcement for fluent speech, the people in his home need reinforcement for their helping behavior. Give it to them.

B. Home, School, and Work

The number of activities, reinforcements, etc., in these environments is gradually reduced.

People in the client's environment who have been trained to work with the client should also gradually attenuate what they are doing.

C. Self-Control

Self-control will gradually reduce as the client continues to maintain fluency.

We have not really "taught" self-control as a separate step, but instead have subsumed it in a number of different steps. By teaching the client to count the number of words on which he stutters and to control his fluency, the program has helped him to become his own monitor and therapist. He has learned to give himself the appropriate instructions and reinforcement.

Illustration No. 4. For Stan, the maintenance program included weekly meetings with the speech therapist near his home, weekly tape recordings made with his family and sent to the University Clinic for analysis, and periodic visits to the University Clinic. These visits totalled 45 hours over a 9 month period. The tape recordings revealed a gradual increase in stuttering rate up to 8 stuttered words per minute. He and his parents also reported that his speech was even less fluent in natural situations than it was during the tape recording sessions and that some situations were still extremely difficult for him. As a result, we saw him again the following summer for an additional 95 hours of instruction. Throughout many varied speaking situations, including a speech to a meeting of over 100 speech therapists, he demonstrated fluency at a rate of less than 0.5 stuttered words per minute. In the following year, the maintenance program included tape recordings twice a week, telephone calls, periodic visits to the University Clinic, and no more local speech therapy. These activities were then faded out toward the end of the year. Altogether, there were 13 hours of tape recording and 29 telephone calls. This new low rate continued in a wide variety of speaking situations, including debating, leading prayers in church, etc., and has continued for the last 6 months. The present maintenance program consists of monthly post cards and yearly clinic visits.

Stan's program was a little different from the program described in this chapter because Stan was one of the first people whom we put through the entire program, and we did not know at that time what steps were necessary, how long to keep him at various steps, and so on. Altogether, more than 225 hours were devoted to Stan's program, and we are not through yet. It is only fair to note that part of this time resulted from our lack of experience; not all of it was due to Stan's stuttering. Our more recent programs are usually shorter.

The program described above is only one of many possible ones. Although the establishment phase contains many elements that are found in many other programs, we do not know yet whether we should use one basic program with a few individual variations or a wide variety of totally different programs for different people. We have observed that the program described in this chapter worked with a number of stutterers who were quite different from each other.

Regardless of the type of establishment program that is used, the transfer and maintenance programs are similar, although there are many possible variations. For example, some people may need more steps, others less (particularly children). Also, the length and schedule of the maintenance program will vary, depending on how severe the stuttering is and how near the client is to the therapist.

We hope that we have given you an idea of how an operant program is put together and administered. We have tried to show some of the variations on the basic theme, and we have tried to show just what the basic theme is. We hope that your appetite has been whetted and that you will try to find out more about the use of operant programs for the treatment of stuttering.

References

Ryan, B. P., "The Establishment, Transfer, and Maintenance of Fluent Reading and Speaking in a Stutterer Using Operant Technology. A paper presented at the Annual Convention of the American Speech and Hearing Association, Denver, November 1968.

Ryan, B. P., "Operant Technology Applied to Stuttering Therapy for Children." A paper presented at the Annual Convention of the American Speech and Hearing Association, Chicago 1969.

Ryan, B. P., "The Construction and Evaluation of a Program for Modifying Stuttering Behavior." Unpublished doctoral dissertation, University of Pittsburgh, 1964.

Sloane, H. W., and MacAulay, B. D. (Eds.), *Operant Procedures in Remedial Speech and Language Training*. Boston: Houghton Mifflin, 1968.

Van Riper, C., *Speech Correction: Principles and Methods*, 4th Ed. Englewood Cliffs, N.J.: Prentice-Hall, 1963.

A Behavioral Analysis of a Stuttering Therapy

P. HELBERT DAMSTE, M.D., Ph. D.

Introduction

The other therapies discussed in this book have been devised on the basis of learning principles. Their history of growth is more experimental than therapeutic. When one of these therapies is used, the therapist and the patient participate equally in a procedure that is very much like an experiment to test if the theory of behavior is right. Consequently, the behavior therapist often manipulates only one thing at a time, and then evaluates the result.

The therapy described in this chapter, however, has a different history. In this case, the therapy preceded the theory. This therapeutic program was developed over the years by Theo Schoenaker, a speech therapist whose primary interest was the treatment of stuttering. By varying his approach and critically appraising the results, Schoenaker developed a form of treatment. The theory came later, to analyze the therapy. It was in fact only in recent years that we contacted the behavior therapists, who had then just started to use their techniques with stutterers. They admired our efficiency in treating stuttering, and we admired their backbone of learning principles. We have been working together ever since. The theory has not only explained the dynamics of therapy, it has also enriched and intensified the method of treatment. Also, there is a wealth of material for the theorist in the therapy program.

As a medical speech pathologist, I feel that it is my task to combine behavioral and physiological explanations. Moreover, I think the era of negative reaction to subjective psychology is sufficiently far behind us so that we can reintroduce the subjective experiences of patients as a source of information on habit-strength, the history of rewarding experiences, and the degree to which situations are felt to be threatening. This permits us to admit into the discussion the subjectively defined feelings which correspond to physiologically defined emotions.

Learning theory explanations of stuttering, especially the two-factor theory developed by Brutten and described in an earlier chapter of this book, explain very well what goes on in our group therapy for stuttering. When we discovered this, we considered it a breakthrough of some importance. For our American readers, we should add that in western Europe, stuttering is still thought by most to be either an organic brain disorder or a mental disturbance to be described in psychoanalytical terms. Consequently, speech therapy for stutterers is not valued very highly. It is something to be tried,

77

even though the expectation of success is small. Scientific interest in speech pathology, both within and without the medical profession, is still limited. Considering that these attitudes are prevalent in Europe, the American reader will understand why behavior therapy is considered by some to be a disturbing nuisance, although it is greeted by others with great enthusiasm.

We, however, have welcomed changes in our therapy program suggested by learning theory, and we have adopted many behavior modification techniques, but we do not throw out older techniques that have proven successful. Let me give one example of an idea that may be foreign to behavior therapists. In the literature on behavior modification, we have found little recognition of the fact that a warm and reassuring environment is favorable for behavior modification. Many of our stutterers, however, are convinced that it is the atmosphere of love and encouragement and the positive attitude toward life in Schoenaker's institute that have made it possible for them to make the necessary adjustments. In due time, we will test the validity of this assumption by comparing the results of various therapists.

We have noticed, in contrast, that in many other therapy programs for stutterers a cool, distant relationship often prevails. I do not know whether this is a matter of principle or simply a result of the therapist's personality. Perhaps both explanations are correct—one can adjust one's theory to one's personality.

Our program also differs from most strictly behavioral therapies in that we are concerned with internal events. We get at internal events in two ways. First, for research purposes, we are interested in the physiology of stuttering, and we therefore regularly record the heart rate, the skin conductance, and the respiration. Occasionally, we use these measures to try and explain why the organism responds as it does. Second, when we practice therapy, we are not content with observing just the objective appearance of events. We are trying to get inside the stutterer in order to know what internal changes are contingent on external stimuli. We do this by talking to the stutterer and trying to understand him as one human being understands another. The information we get from these two techniques is used to install an early warning system designed to prevent inappropriate tensions.

The two-factor theory explains that the autonomic responses (tension and anxiety) produce a disruption of speech. The instrumental responses are an attempt to escape or avoid this disruption. We feel that the instrumental responses, after having been long established, become conditioned stimuli giving rise to more tension. To break this vicious cycle, we attack the autonomic and the instrumental responses simultaneously. We interrupt or prevent the act of stuttering and bring the autonomic responses that interfere with other functions back to a normal level by releasing tension and

78

controlling breathing. We systematically reward this "stop, then release" response. By so doing, we instil in the stutterer a new habit: he becomes able to react to each situation with adequate tonus and excitability. Whenever he feels an internal signal that tension is excessive, he will release it; and whenever he percieves that tension is insufficient (for example, he is sitting sprawled in a chair during an important lecture) he will adjust his tonus to a degree appropriate to the situation.

The Effect of Emotion on Muscle Tonus

It will be helpful to explain the physiology of muscle tonus here. Most striated muscles are controlled by three types of nerve fibers. The first type consists of the alpha fibers, which transmit messages from the medulla to the muscle, telling it to contract. The second type of nerve sends signals in the opposite direction, specifically, from the muscle spindle or stretch receptors, back to the medulla. In essence, these nerves tell the medulla that the muscle is stretching. These two types of nerves operate together after the manner of a feedback loop, so that when a force is applied to the muscle so that it is passively stretched, this fact is signalled to the medulla, which in turn signals back to the muscle to contract. This sequence of events produces the familiar stretch reflex. This entire feedback system can be made either more or less sensitive by the third type of nerve, the gamma nerve. These are thin nerves, issuing from the medulla, and connected to tiny musclelike fibers that make up the muscle spindle. These tiny fibers are contractile, like muscle tissue, and when contracted they change the shape of the spindle into exactly the same shape that it has when the entire muscle is stretched. Consequently, when these tiny fibers are contracted, it takes very little stretch of the muscle to cause a signal to be sent to the medulla indicating that stretching is taking place. The gamma system, then, controls how ready the muscle is to react. This readiness is what we call tonus. Figure 1 illustrates the control of striate muscle tonus.

When the organism is aroused and alert and tension is high, the gamma system is highly excited, the fibers of the muscle spindle are contracted, and the tonus of the muscle is high.

The Effect of Emotion on Breathing Patterns

Of course, arousal and tension affect more than just the tonus of muscles. In addition to having muscles that are ready to flex, arousal produces in us a change in the blood volume distribution, dilation of the eye pupils, palmar sweat, and affects the "semi-autonomic" response of breathing.

In situations that are familiar, tranquil, and not out of the ordinary, there is what might be described as a "peaceful" emotional

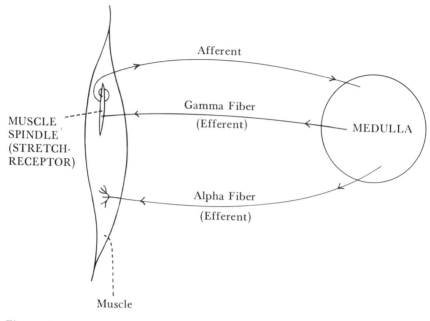

Figure 1. The Control of Striate Muscle Tonus (A signal in the gamma fiber produces an effect "as if" the muscle itself had been stretched. This produces increased readiness for contraction).

response. In such a situation, there is predominantly diaphragmatic respiration. This can be observed by the fact that the movements of breathing take place in the lower abdominal region. With rising tension, however, movements of the chest become apparent. In a state of high tension, such as an emergency, in which the emotional response might be described as either aggressive or fearful, there is even more high thoracic breathing. Sometimes the abdomen is held stiff or even performs reverse movements. In such a state, there may also be constriction in the pharynx and larynx. This entire complex reaction of hypertensive breathing may become conditioned to anxiety-arousing stimuli.

The Active Regulation of Tonus

Because a disturbed breathing pattern is often an obvious part of stuttering, "breathing exercises" have been used for many years in programs of stuttering therapy. In the past, incompetent practice has often brought discredit, fallaciously, on the technique.

Since the breathing pattern is very sensitive to different degrees of tension, the internal stimuli associated with respiration can be used by the stutterer as he learns to monitor the degree of his tension. He is taught to react to the slightest sign of increasing tension by voluntarily releasing tension just as he prepares to speak. In this way, he learns to change his habitual, hypertensive way of responding to speech situations.

With these techniques, the stutterer is able to both diminish his tension in speaking situations and improve his speech performance. Both of these changes are learned if rewards, such as feelings of self-control and fluent speech, are experienced contingent on controlled breathing and release of tension. At the Schoenaker center, where residential treatment is provided, these new habits are called "speaking on the flow," and they are established only after much practice and rehearsal. In daily life, this new habit will have to compete with older established habits of behavior. How successfully the new habit is maintained then will depend on the degree to which the old habit has been extinguished.

Therapy Procedures

The therapeutic procedure is begun with an eight-day course, during which the stutterer receives seven hours of active therapy each day in a residential setting. The purpose of this intensive treatment is to give the stutterer a large quantity of corrective experiences within a short time. During this eight-day course, we present to the stutterer many varied positive environmental and internal stimuli in order to reverse the cycle of negative expectation and consequences. We are trying to reverse the negativity of environmental and internal stimuli by embedding the threatening signals in pleasant or positive stimulation.

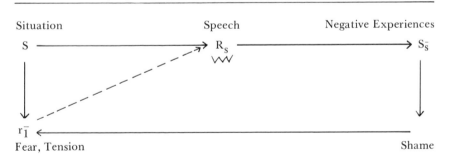

Figure 2. A Two-Factor Model of Stuttering. From G. J. Brutten and D. J. Shoemaker, *The Modification of Stuttering* (Englewood Cliffs, N. J.: Prentice-Hall, Inc.). The figure has been slightly modified to correct an illogicality.

Figure 2 illustrates Brutten and Shoemaker's two-factor theory of stuttering. A situation (S) results in negative emotion (r_1^-). Speech behavior (R_S) is disrupted and becomes dysfluent ($\sim\!\!\sim$). The effect of r^- on R_S is not learned, so that the arrow connecting the two symbols is dashed. Solid arrows indicate a learned or conditioned

81

effect. The stuttered speech (R_s) brings about, through negative listener reactions and negative internal reactions, a number of negative stimuli associated with speech that impinge on the stutterer (S_s^-). These stimuli, of course, produce more negative emotion $(r_{\bar{2}})$, such as shame and guilt. The negative emotions of shame and guilt summate with the negative emotion of fear and result in the negative expectation which accompanies almost every speaking situation.

Using the Brutten and Shoemaker model, we would diagram the therapeutic procedures outlined in this chapter as shown in Figure 3.

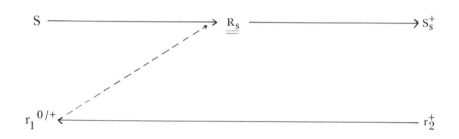

Figure 3. A Model of Therapy Procedures

By teaching the stutterer how to control tension we enable him to speak fluently $(r^{0/+}\ -\!-R_s)$, and to approach his listeners without fear (See number 6 of the next section). The fluent speech causes the group to react positively and it causes the individual to react positively, so that stimulation associated with speaking changes from minus to plus (S_s^+). As this occurs, both hope and confidence are restored, along with self-respect (r_2^+). When added to the neutral expectancy, which was induced at the beginning, these changes will result in a more positive state of expectancy, that is, $r_1^{\,0/+}$ and r_2^+ equal r^+. It should be noted here that in our view, when learning takes place, it is not only behavior that changes, but neuronal organization and its subjective aspect, self-concept and body image, as well. The two learning processes and the effects they have on neuronal organization and self-concept and body image are illustrated in Figure 4.

One of the techniques we use to make these changes in the value of stimuli and responses is desensitization. The therapy we provide takes place on a broad spectrum of behavior, and we manipulate many variables at the same time. It will be helpful, however, to list here several of the hierarchies we use in desensitization.

Learning Processes	Neuronal Organization	Self-Concept and Body Image
Classical conditioning	Control of emotional responding	Feelings, attitudes
Instrumental Conditioning	Sensorimotor reactions (adjustment to environment)	Sensory and motor experiences, the proprioceptive representation of behavior

Figure 4. The Two Learning Processes and Two Aspects of Their Effect.

The first of these hierarchies gradually increases the degree of alertness that must be maintained for the situation. When we first taught the new response of releasing tensions and "speaking on the flow," the stutterers were in a supine position. In the first hierarchy they proceed from the supine position to a situation in which they are standing up and addressing a group.

Hierarchy A

1. Supine, all speaking at once, not taking notice of one another.
2. Sitting or standing, same as above.
3. Sitting or standing, speaking one at a time, listening to each other.
4. Standing or sitting, speaking to one other member of the group, the others doing the same (in pairs).
5. Standing, speaking to one other person, the others listening.
6. Standing, speaking to the group.

In another hierarchy we systematically increase the length and content of the spoken phrases.

Hierarchy B

1. Short phrases, the stutterer describes his own bodily experiences during relaxation.
2. The phrases are kept short and are meaningless (nonsense phrases).
3. Long nonsense phrases are spoken.
4. Communicative speech.

These two hierarchies are combined by having the stutterers practice the items in B in each of the situations of A. In this way, all possible combinations of A and B are covered.

There are, however, many other hierarchies which we also use. In one of these, we systematically increase the degree to which listener reaction is a negative stimulus.

1. Benevolent listeners.
2. Critical listeners.
3. Demanding listeners.
4. Frightening or threatening listeners.

This hierarchy can also be combined with A and B. For example, during one of the last steps of Hierarchy A, the stutterers in the group change their behavior in accordance with Hierarchy C while the patient changes his behavior in accordance with Hierarchy B. It must be noted that each of the items of Hierarchy C are either low or high in the patient's total hierarchy depending on the relative dominance with which the patient sees his relationship to his listeners. This, then, becomes another hierarchy.

Hierarchy D

1. Strongly dominant.
2. Moderately dominant.
3. Equal
4. Moderately submissive.
5. Strongly submissive.

A, B, and C were hierarchies that were roughly valid for the whole group but D is a highly personal hierarchy. We have not been using D except when the patient discovers the importance of this variable for himself. The first individual hierarchy of speaking situations is usually composed by all members of the group around the fourth day of therapy (see number 13 of the next section). Each item of the personal hierarchy is then worked on as follows (see also number 14 of the next section):

1.   The patient imagines the situation as it might be anticipated with positive feelings.
2.   The patient writes a report of the situation as he anticipates it, in positive language.
3.   He reads the report aloud, and it is discussed by the group.
4.   The situation is presented orally to the group as it is anticipated with positive feelings.
5.   The patient actually performs the situation for the group.
6.   The patient reports orally to the group his actual experience with the situation, as interpreted in positive terms.

It should be noted that not all of the steps of this procedure have been mentioned in this list. During the time that a patient is working on his personal hierarchy, much suggestion and persuasion comes from the group and the therapist in order for the patient to be able to produce a report with positive anticipation.

Learning principles go a long way to help us explain what goes on in therapy. We feel that therapy for stuttering must include a full range of human activity, from gaining control over the most elemental body functions (autonomic as well as sensorimotor) to gaining control over thoughts and self-concepts and attitudes toward other human beings.

An Actual Therapy Program

What follows is a series of comments made by the patient and the therapist on each section of the therapy program.

1. Introduction

My name is Albert. I'm nineteen years old and rather big, athletic you might say. I'm about to leave college and enter the university. In general, I am good humored and socially well accepted, despite my stuttering, which is rather severe. I have had many different kinds of treatment for my stuttering, all of which have been unsuccessful, so that you can understand why I look forward to this new program with mixed feelings. Of course, I will give them my full cooperation, but I can't help being a little sceptical.

Behavior that has become habitual can be reliably predicted to occur in the presence of particular external and internal stimuli. Because of the stability of these habitual responses, many stutterers are comparatively well adjusted, even those with hideous forms of stuttering. For such stutterers, better speech is not rewarding in itself. It is even less rewarding if, in order to attain it, highly treasured personal vices, such as self-reproach and self-pity must be given up. These difficulties make it all the more important to work toward the end goal, which is modification of the habitual behavior, through a number of smaller and well-defined sub-goals. This procedure of scaling down the end goal to a series of sub-goals makes it possible to identify specific behaviors that need to be learned. These behaviors can then be practiced and reinforced.

2. First Contact and the Clinical Environment

About four months ago, I made my first visit to the clinic. At that time, I had a brief medical examination and was referred to a speech therapist for an interview. I was surprised how much this man seemed to understand about my problem, and I was pleased by the frank and straightforward manner in which he discussed it. My first impression was that he is somebody who does not let himself be fooled, by me or by anybody else. Somehow, this gave me the feeling that I had found the right man.

Everybody feels most secure inside familiar habits. When such habits are changed, and we abandon the safety of established behavior, we enter a period of vulnerability and uncertainty. We regress to a state in which we are more dependent on others, although this regression is only temporary. When a lobster reaches that time when it must shed its old shell, it goes into a sheltered place to do so, and when it comes out, it is stronger than it was before. Similarly, the stutterer who is about to make profound personal readjustments must have complete confidence in his therapist, both as an expert in his field and as a person who can offer

85

protection. So, the warm and reassuring atmosphere of the clinical environment is important because it offers the stutterer a needed feeling of security. It is also important to maintain this atmosphere because a smile from someone you respect and admire is more rewarding than one from someone else. There are therapists who are afraid to establish such a warm relationship in which they become personally involved with their patients. When parents act this way, we realize that they are ill-informed. They have not yet discovered that children who explore from a secure and loving environment grow up to be independent and capable of loving others, but that children reared in loveless surroundings will lack confidence and courage. The same principle holds for the different kind of growth and the different kind of exploring experienced by stutterers in therapy. Positive expectations, encouragement, and reward are better methods for supporting adaptive behavior than fear, avoidance, and punishment.

3. The Pre-Treatment Examination

In August, 1967, I was notified that I should come to the clinic for two days of examination, testing, and recordings. I went to the clinic, and at the end of the two-day period there was an interview in which I was told that I could participate in a therapy program. This program consists of twelve days of residential treatment, one eight-day period followed after three weeks by a four-day period. After that, there are regular, out-patient sessions.

The various examinations allow us to determine whether a patient is acceptable for the therapeutic program and give us research data for later use in determining how effective the program was. The therapist plays no role in these assessment procedures. We require an average or above average intelligence and a personality structure that is not too deviant. Some personalities may create problems and hinder the progress of the group. We realize, however, that people with such deviant personalities may also profit considerably by participating in a positively oriented group, and as a result we are more likely to accept them than to exclude them. We do, however, take extra care to assign them to a group in which the personality structures of the other patients will lead the way to adjustment, and in which the leader is experienced.

4. Group Responsibility in Determining Sub-Goals

On the first day, the members of the group meet each other. Whenever I have to say my name I have a good block, but so do they. There are eight of us in all, so that we have to say our names seven times. After we have all arrived, tape recordings are made of each of us as we read out loud and speak freely. After the recordings have been made, the therapist asks us what features are common to all of the stutterers in the group. After some discussion we agree that tension and word fears are shared by all. Since it seems useful to practice the release of tension, we decide to try this out.

From now on it will be the group that makes the essential decisions about the activities and assignments that are to be done.

86

The therapist will present to them all of the possible exercises and practices that they might do, and they will choose those that they find most useful. Thus, very early, they have to assume the responsibility for the effectiveness of their treatment. Of course, the therapist guides this process, although he does so nondirectively. During the first session, the participants become acquainted with relaxation practice.

5. Relaxation and Breath Control

Blankets are spread out on the floor, and we lie down, each in his own area. The therapist presents two themes: (1) Tension is a way of reacting to the environment. Now retreat into yourself; close your eyes. (2) The tensions we want to control and eventually eliminate are generated within the limits of our own bodies. Therefore, be conscious of your body, define its borders, and try to concentrate your attention on everything within them. Different parts of the body are being scanned for several qualities: weight, temperature, movements. We also direct our attention to the automatic movements of breathing and heart beat. We can diminish the tension in the organism by directing our attention to the expiratory phase of breathing. Sounds are then produced on the flow of expiration, and later words and sentences are spoken by the group together.

We believe that instead of talking the stutterer out of his false beliefs and misinterpretations, it is more effective to reconstruct his notions about himself and his environment by exposing him to a carefully selected succession of subjective experiences. In this first relaxation session, he learns that he can be the master of his own tension, of his flow of breath, and of his speech. He will reconfirm this lesson many times as he practices these same exercises daily. It is not difficult to experience the fact that tension release is achieved most easily during the expiratory phase of breathing.*

6. Experimenting with Fluency Control

On the second day, the tension-control session is spent with a further survey of the sensations involved in the process of breathing. The therapist says a sentence, and we say it after him, everyone in his own time, and at the moment that is appropriate for him. For example, "I feel the movement of my breath." (The group repeats the sentence.) "I notice the air entering through my nose." (The group repeats.) "I feel my trunk expanding a little." (Repeat.) "I pay attention to the peak of inspiration." (Repeat.) "I make the transition from inspiration to expiration a fluent one." (Repeat.) "When inspiration is at its peak, I begin speaking." (Repeat.) "When my phrase is finished, I let the remaining air run off, sshhh." (Repeat.) "Then I wait for the next inspiratory phase to occur, and I let it flow in without any tension." (Repeat.) "This way of speaking makes me relaxed and gives me confidence." (Repeat.) "Thus I continuously increase my self-reliance." (Repeat.) All of us in the group feel satisfied after this session because we have penetrated further into one of the roots of the stuttering problem. We stretch and yawn uninhibitedly before we get up.

---

*Bishop (1968), in her experiments with cats, indicated that the excitability of the motor system falls off just after the peak of the inspiratory phase.

In this tension-control session, when everyone is relaxed and stretched out on the floor with their eyes closed, no one in the group will have any trouble with fluency. Their minds are essentially occupied observing the respiratory events in their own bodies, so that hardly any attention is paid to the environment, much less to possible listeners' reactions. This experience of being with others in one room and pronouncing fluent phrases is very gratifying. And this is the beginning of reciprocal inhibition; in this, the lowest step of the desensitization ladder, the conditioned reactions of halting and blocking in the presence of others is countered by applying tension-release and breath control. Pronouncing phrases describing what is being observed in the body serves two functions: (1) focusing the attention on a body part trains the body image, and (2) experiencing the automatic flow of words establishes a firm association between the internal stimuli of tension-control and fluent speech.

7. Rewarding the Sub-Goal in Dialogue Situations

During supper on the first day, I notice that people already feel more free to stutter. I catch Henk trying to substitute an easier word for one he is having difficulty with, and he is not even angry and joins in the laughter. A conversation develops in which we each exchange some of the tricks we use and ways we have of avoiding difficulty. Somebody at the table tells a joke on this theme. The atmosphere is social, and people are less afraid to stutter. Someone even tries to solve a block by releasing tension and speaking on the flow. The result is unsatisfactory, but the therapist uses the incident as an example and shows that this is the beginning of the road to success. The attempt is repeated, and I try to follow the example. The therapist seems to notice and nods his approval.

The principles of operant conditioning are used to develop the new behavior. The first reaction the stutterer must master is a preventive one. He must learn to stop as soon as he notices the approach of a block; only then will he be able to prevent stuttering. Once the habitual response has been broken by stopping, the stutterer releases tension and speaks on the flow. Since active control of tension and controlled breathing are antagonistic to anxiety, stuttering blocks cannot occur. The good new responses are rewarded. In the beginning we reward all attempts to stop before a block occurs, but later only the successful attempts are rewarded, and finally reward is given only when tension control and fluent speech occur.

The nature of the reward also changes during the course of treatment. At first, the therapist simply shows his approval. Shortly thereafter, the group also reacts, showing its approval, accepting the individual as one of the group, and occasionally even showing admiration. Toward the end, the stutterer experiences self-confidence, security, and self-respect. He no longer feels doubt or any other negative emotion in situations that used to be extremely unpleasant. These last rewards are the strongest reinforcers.

The strong desire to stay within the safety of familiar old habits must be outweighed by the strongest positive experiences. The newcomer will be afraid of almost anything new, and he must be sufficiently assured and rewarded so that he will abandon his habitual behavior. The early rewards of therapist and group approval may seem to be an infantile sort of gratification, but it is only a temporary stage. The final rewards of increased positive feelings are permanent because they are not bound to either the therapist or the group. These reinforcers are sensations within the individual himself. Consequently, the response brings its own reward, as if a closed circuit had been developed through conditioning. As soon as this stage has been reached, the patient may continue to develop a great deal with much more independence.

8. Functions of the Group.

The patient had no comment on this section.

The clinical sessions serve as a preparation for the tasks the stutterer will eventually work on in everyday life. These tasks are graded in a hierarchy of increasingly more difficult steps, and the sequence of the steps must not be altered. There are three variables that seem to affect the difficulty of each of these steps and consequently are responsible for the degree of tension experienced in the situation. First, the tension increases with the number of people present and to the degree that the stutterer perceives those people as dominant over him. Second, the tension varies with the attitude of the listeners, whether they are kindly disposed, critical, or threatening. And third, tension varies with the patient's own feelings, whether he is confident, doubtful, or uncertain. Our initial practice of tension-release and other behaviors used to arrive at fluent speech takes place in the easiest circumstances; the patient is "hypnotized" into having complete confidence in himself, and his listening environment is similarly influenced into showing all of the signs of a benevolent attitude. After two or three weeks go by, however, we are at a much higher level and the conditions are much different. The group may have attacked the patient about some dubious character trait, and this may make the patient somewhat uncertain about himself. Furthermore, he finds that the therapist is not at his side in the battle that follows. Two things may happen: He may retain his composure using the tension-release, the controlled breathing, and the positive inner attitude he has been practicing. If this occurs, it will be an enormous reinforcement of these behaviors. But, on the other hand, he may not succeed; he may lose his nerve and start blocking. In that case, the group will very quickly change its policy. Someone will signal his encouragement, another one will come to assist him in regaining control of his breathing, and the therapist will also do something to restore the patient's confidence. Pretty soon he will get another chance to show that he has made progress and is able to apply the techniques. Whatever the outcome, the positive atmosphere of mutual friendship and encouragement makes it impossible for any severe punishing experiences to occur. This is important because such experiences would retard the development of a positive and confident inner attitude.

9. Stimulus Generalization and Carryover into Life Situations

During meals and discussions, the members of the group constantly remind each other to make use of the new techniques. If not carefully managed, the old automatic behaviors will maintain themselves. The patient often requests other members of the group to intervene and remind him of these things. He may be reminded to maintain an upright sitting posture, to control his breathing, to release his tension, or to sustain the flow of speech on continued expiration. This complex new behavior, which takes the place of the old block can be summarized as "stop, release, speak on the breathflow."

"Relaxation exercises" have little value in and of themselves, unless they lead to tension-control during an increasing number of everyday life situations. Speech may be fluent in the presence of the therapist, but what will happen in more demanding surroundings? People who thwart your attempt to take your time and get your tension under control will succeed in throwing you off balance. And there will be other minor difficulties. Some of these difficulties are met by the gradual process of systematic desensitization. But of course we cannot desensitize the patient to all of the stimuli he will ever meet. Consequently, it is necessary to depend on the principle of *stimulus generalization*. According to this principle, desensitization will take place not only to those stimuli experienced in the therapy situation, but also to stimuli which resemble those experienced in the clinic. Furthermore, the degree to which the desensitization will generalize to similar stimuli is dependent upon the similarity between the stimuli in the clinic and those in everyday life. Consequently, we make an effort to make life in the therapy center during the residential period as close as possible to the situations that are encountered outside the clinic.

10. The Informing Stimulus

All members of the group carry in their pockets a toy whistle with which they remind each other to maintain the new response. A squeak from this whistle means that you are forgetting one or more of the responses involved in speaking on the flow. As soon as someone is caught in the act of indulging in his old habit, he will receive squeaks as a friendly reminder to relax and speak on the flow.

One of the important principles of behavior modification is that correction must be applied immediately, right at the moment when the incorrect response occurs. Only when the correction occurs during or immediately after the response is it a help. Otherwise, if it comes later, it is perceived as a reproach or criticism, and may damage the patient's motivation. The stutterer hears only too often the phrase "It would have been better had you done it this way," or "Next time, do so and so." Discussions after the event are no good—the sensorimotor experience is past and has already left its mark. Immediate correction is the only way to handle errors so that the wrong engram is not laid down. The incorrect response is interrupted and the action resumed along the correct way of responding. Because correction must occur during and not after the incorrect behavior has occurred, the therapist alone cannot supply the necessary stimulation. He sets the tone, but the group members follow his example and provide the signal that an incorrect behavior is occurring. The squeak signal is therefore considered by the patients not as a punishment, but as a mutual brotherly assistance for which they are grateful. It is an informative stimulus inviting behavior change.

11. Positive Suggestion as a Catalyst

On the third day, one of the members brought up a discussion subject in the evening session. He said "The formulas about releasing the flow of speech seem perfectly credible at the moment when I speak them. That is, when I have taken the time to prepare myself in advance by concentrating on breathing in a controlled way. But at other times, when I have been stuttering badly, and can feel my throat contracting, these formulas seem ridiculous." The therapist explained how suggestion works. He said that it is a powerful technique for bringing your subconsciously controlled automatic behaviors into conscious control. "But," the therapist went on, "automatic habits will respond to suggestion only if, at the moment when you are trying to suggest a state of mind to youself, you are practicing what you say. If the formula is only repeated in a magical fashion, it will indeed be ridiculous. It will only work when it reflects the state of your mind and body. Your certainty, however, will grow with the amount of practicing that you do."

This scene is a prelude to a scene that will occur again and again—our thoughts influence our actions and vice versa. Consequently, we must reverse the direction of our pessimistic thinking. But how can it be done? The formulas that the student found ridiculous are a technique for introducing a desirable response. The positive idea itself makes possible some control over behavior, and this will lead to more positive responses, which in turn act as stimuli for further control. The words, the formulas, act as messengers of thoughts that are related to positive experiences. When recalled, these formulas carry with them a certain amount of positive expectation. This is what we mean by suggestion, and most therapies use it in one way or another. Gradually, with repetition, it will become easier to evoke the positive expectation. The formulas are then used to get into the desired attitude in a short period of time. Later, when the old habits have been abandoned, and new ones have replaced them, these suggestive formulas have lost their function and are forgotten. They are useful only as temporary devices, as catalysts that accelerate the process of learning.

12. Desensitization to Stuttering Itself

After five or six days of training, we have become utterly overconfident. Our optimism is strong, our expectations high, and we all think we will soon be rid of our stuttering. Life without stuttering will present no problems. When we take part, however, in real-life situations outside the training center, we undergo our first disappointments. We are sent on assignments into situations where we have to stutter voluntarily. We go in pairs, one checking the other. These assignments are designed to test our sensitivity to our stuttering. All of us report that we profoundly dislike the assignment. Did the people we spoke to react unkindly? No, but the old fear of stuttering dominated, and it aroused the old feelings of shame that we thought we were rid of, and the old reactions to these feelings and the attempts to overcome them returned too. We felt as if we were sinking back into a quagmire after having momentarily reached dry ground.

In some ways, stuttering may be compared to an allergy. Under ordinary circumstances, the body develops antigens to defend itself against foreign material. With repeated intrusions of foreign material, the antigens develop more and more rapidly. In the case of allergy, however, this mechanism overshoots its purpose; it might be defined as oversensitivity or overreaction to a relatively harmless foreign material. In behavioral terms, it is certainly normal and perhaps healthy to react to the criticisms of others, just as the body reacts to foreign materials. For the stutterer, however, the reaction is too extensive for the relatively harmless negative reactions of others to the dysfluencies in his own speech. Furthermore, the stutterer's reactions, like antigens, develop more rapidly with repeated criticism. By extending this analogy further, we might consider voluntary stuttering, which is introduced when the treatment is well underway, as an immunological desensitization. The analogy may be further extended, in that the dosages of voluntary stuttering increase. The first dosages of voluntary stuttering are administered daily in the center, in a situation in which the patients have been trained to switch their stuttering on and off in the presence of each other and occasionally in the presence of visitors. The step into the outside world, however, is a big one and requires extensive preparation, which is described in the following paragraphs. In the meantime, however, life goes on, and the stutterer goes to work or to school, where he will have to face situations for which he has not been desensitized. Consequently, by decreasing his sensitivity to his own stuttering, we have removed one of the causes of frustration, and we have made progress toward fluency, and progress is rewarding.

At any point in desensitization therapy there are certain situations that remain sufficiently severe in terms of the anxiety they induce so that the stutterer is nonfluent in them. For such situations, we teach the stutterer to use forms of modified nonfluent speech. In this way, a technique of successive approximation is used, while, at the same time, the level of situational stress at which fluency occurs is being raised by desensitization. The relationship of these two techniques to each other is illustrated in Figure 5.

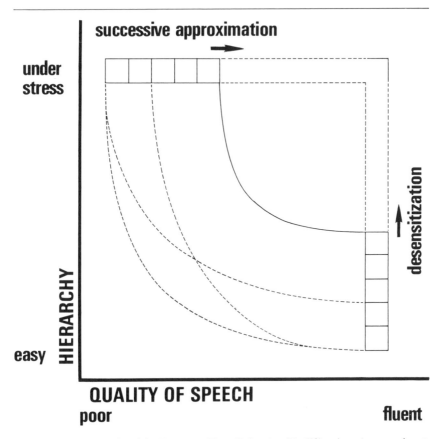

Figure 5. The Relationship Between Two Behavior Modification Approaches to Stuttering Therapy.

Successive approximation is begun in stressful situations. Initially, any variation of the habitual stuttering pattern is rewarded, but by differential reinforcement, the therapist aims at a modified form of nonfluent speech that approaches fluency. *Desensitization* begins at the level of situation—induced stress at which fluency occurs. If necessary, this level of relaxation is induced by means of suggestion or hypnosis. The level of situation-induced stress at which fluency occurs is then raised by exposing the patient to successively more stressful situations, during each of which he learns to control his autonomic reactions of tension and fear.

Successive approximation is primarily an operant procedure, although it achieves secondary gains in the emotional area. Desensitization is primarily a deconditioning of emotional reactions, combined with a simultaneous reprogramming of speech habits.

13. The Hierarchy of Situations

When we confronted life outside the clinic, we found that it was much more difficult to use our newly learned response of stopping, releasing tension, and speaking on the flow, than it had been within the walls of the clinic. As a result of this experience, all of us composed a list of situations ranging from the most easy to the most difficult.

Desensitization should be performed as gradually as possible, and this is accomplished through the use of a *hierarchy* of situations. We present to the stutterer a standard series of situations, and he rates them on a five-point scale for each of the following questions: (1) how frequently the situation occurs, (2) how severely he stutters in the situation, (3) whether he likes or does not like to speak in the situation, and (4) whether he is inclined or not to avoid the situation. The standard list* can be supplemented with more situations to bridge possible gaps or to deal with special problems.

14. The Positive Situation Description

Just as we first learned to prepare our phrases and speeches in the group, we now learn to prepare for the situation that is next on our hierarchy. After I have released tension, either in supine or sitting position, I try to experience the situation in my imagination as vividly as possible, including all of the accompanying details I might expect. I do not avoid any details, but I look at the situation in a positive way and describe the positive aspects of everything that I expect to come my way.

The description is written down and read out loud to the group. Later, it is related in a spontaneous monologue in which all of the pleasant thoughts and feelings that may accompany the situation are expressed. Neither negative ideas nor their denials are permitted in the description (for example, "I feel no fear."), nor are verbs in the past tense or words expressing doubts or wishes (for example, "I try to be cheerful."). The description is clear-cut and precise; the exact place and time of the situation and the exact localization of objects and persons in it are described.

When one of the group fails to present a positive situation description in a way convincing to himself or his audience, the group concludes that he is too high on his hierarchy and has to come down to an easier situation. As soon as a situation is described positively and successfully, in that the author remains relaxed and fluent during his description, the situation can be practiced in reality.

This technique of presenting successive situations by having the stutterer read them out loud has some interesting theoretical implications. In the technique of systematic desensitization as described by Wolpe, the anxiety-arousing situations are presented to the patient by having him imagine the situation while his state of relaxation is maintained. We have modified this technique by having the stutterer describe the situation himself. This is a natural continuation of the exercises described earlier in this chapter in which the stutterer described his experiences of self-observation.

---

*See Johnson, W., Darley, F., and Spriestersbach, D., *Diagnostic Procedures in Speech Pathology*. New York: Harper & Row, 1963.

During this stage, the patient could speak fluently because he was relaxed, but we can reverse this effect and infer the patient's relaxed state from his fluent speech.

A verbal description of the situations in the hierarchy by the patient himself provide the following advantages: (1) The situation is experienced more directly and more realistically if the patient states it in his own words than if it is described by the therapist. Since this results in stimulation that is closer to that in the patient's real life, *stimulus generalization* is increased. (2) Although it is never possible to obtain surveillance over the patient's imagination, the therapist has a better idea of the patient's scene when he hears the patient describing it in his own words. (3) The therapist also has a better idea of the patient's state of relaxation by observing the patient's manner of speaking. Fluent speech indicates that no emotional tension has disturbed the tension-control that the patient is using. Therefore, we may assume, at least in this verbal situation, that the patient has been desensitized. And (4), the fact that the patient experiences without tension a situation that used to be difficult and at the same time finds himself able to speak fluently is valuable in the extinction of fear.

It should be noted that in these descriptions, relaxation is not the only positive force that is used as an antagonist to situational fear. There are also feelings of self-control and self-confidence, confidence in the situation, and in the other members of the group, and there is the desire to speak. We mobilize as many positive stimuli as possible, for in that way we can climb the hierarchy of situations more rapidly. Most patients are sufficiently motivated by the satisfaction they derive from climbing the hierarchy itself. Some, however, need additional encouragement, which is given now and then according to an intermittent schedule.

15. The Demosthenes Organization

If I had a few more pages at my disposal I would relate here all of the good done by the monthly meetings of the local Demosthenes Organization. These meetings have made me continue with daily preparation for difficult situations, and have given me an opportunity to regain hope at moments when otherwise none would have been found.

The follow-up procedure, which begins after two or three periods of residential treatment, is organized largely by former stutterers. They organize regional training groups and training weekends, and play a role in the summer course for young stutterers. Probably the most powerful motivational force to maintain the slow march of improvement through daily practice is the internal satisfaction of becoming the master of an unruly part of oneself and the pride of belonging to an elite group of people who are now conquering where formerly they were losing ground.

95

PART THREE

Examination and Evaluation

In this section we try to evaluate the operant and two-factor learning theory approaches to stuttering therapy. We will try to point out their weaknesses and strengths. It is difficult for the practicing clinician to make this critical appraisal. It was hard for us too, but we felt that criticism may help all of us maintain the objectivity which seems to be required. Learning theory is still in flux. The psychologists argue fiercely about such basic concepts as reward and punishment, drives, stimuli and responses. If this is true about learning theory in general, we can understand why we find conflicting views about how we should treat stuttering. You have now heard the advocates; you have had some opportunity to examine the evidence. Now here come the judges—and alas, we find that they too show some disagreement about the sentence to be imposed.

Stuttering, Behavior Modification, and the Person

ALBERT T. MURPHY, Ph. D.

One's view of stuttering is at least partially derived from a professional or scientific perspective; this perspective, in turn, is part of a broader philosophy of existence and of the nature of man. To try to understand stuttering or to treat stutterers with a perspective any less broad than this makes little sense. The disorder is both too characteristically human and too complex. It makes even less sense at a time like this, when stuttering theories and therapies are apparently experiencing radical change.

Science has a way of hitting man where it hurts him the most. First, the Copernican doctrine removed man from the center of the universe and relegated *his* earth to the position of a minor planet. Second, Darwin's concepts removed man from his privileged position not just above but apart from the other species and placed him in a line of development with the apes. And third, psychoanalysis devastated man's image of himself as rational. Will there be a fourth blow—a technological one—which will completely depersonalize man? I think not. But there are rumblings of concern to the current renascence of behavioristic theories and programs which, more and more, are being applied to behaviorally impaired people by a variety of service professionals including speech clinicians. This chapter is a brief response to both the renascence and the rumble.

Ever since the seventeenth century, when physics was given a scientific foundation, theorists have been trying to build a similar foundation for the psychology of human behavior. The first of these theorists was probably Hobbes, who tried to take the concepts then used to explain the motions of astral bodies and apply them to human behavior. This view was opposed in those days by Descartes, who felt that introspection established the existence of mind *(cogito ergo sum)*. Descartes differentiated man from machines by attributing to man an incorporeal thinking substance. Although incorporeality is not directly related to any modern conception of conscious processes or to stuttering, the Descartes-Hobbes argument is a prototype of today's argument between behaviorists and, let us say, phenomenologists.

In the eighteenth century, philosophical questions were rarely differentiated from psychological ones, and philosophers were trying to develop a science of man. One of these philosophers was David Hume, who held, much as Hobbes did, that thought was invisible and hidden from others. The "association psychologists" considered man a passive being, a *tabula rasa* upon which external events were imprinted. The mind was incapable of initiating thoughts or behavior; any idea or action that occurred was caused by the associations that had been stamped in. As a result, responses depended upon the frequency and sequence of inputs. Since a person's perceptions simply reflected inputs, his description of his own thinking processes was relatively valueless.

Echoes of these early conceptions may be heard throughout this book.

All of these early views considered man as a construction of a number of parts all of which were related to each other in a mechanical way. Emmanuel Kant, in his *Critique of Pure Reason* (1781), developed quite a different point of view. He spoke of desires, affects, and passions, not as blind mechanical pushes from behind but as interests exercised through the will. He felt that man's actions were mediated by meanings, by a consideration of how significant an act or its consequences might be, particularly in a social sense. Kant considered man an active agent, initiating behavior, not just as a passive receiver. A century later, William James was to summarize this idea by saying that "the pull from the future is as real as the push from behind." Since he did not see man in mechanical terms, Kant felt that psychology could never be a true science in the Newtonian sense.

Despite Kant, the traditional mainstream of psychology ended up being empirical, became increasingly experimental, and developed a highly quantitative tradition well known today to all. Its modern basis rests in the behaviorism of John B. Watson, who, half a century ago, held that psychology must discard all references to consciousness. The terms *consciousness, mental states,* or *mind* were not to be used. Instead, all description was to be done in terms of stimulus and response. As one commentator stated, psychology must never use psychological terms!

From then on, stimulus-response or similar behavior theories developed, focussing on events external to the mind. These theories leaned heavily on Pavlov's work on conditioned reflexes, and gradually they came to focus on the problem of learning, or, from their point of view, on the establishment or strengthening of S-R bonds. They studied man as a reactor, not as an actor or an initiating agent. Man's behavior could be understood solely on the basis of the inputs he experienced. Hull *(Principles of Behavior,* 1943) was concerned with the temporal relationship between the response and the stimulus, drive-reduction, and habit strength, and related these variables with keen precision to a large body of experimental work, usually done with animals. He criticised cognitive concepts, such as consciousness, as "subjective." He wanted to establish precise correlations between physical stimuli and responses free of the encumbrances of mentalistic concepts. He tried to explain behavior

100

by relating it to the consistency with which different events in the past were associated with one another.

Today, the chief spokesman for the positivistic view is Harvard's B. F. Skinner, who has focussed recently on a one-factor learning analysis of behavior, operant conditioning. His pioneering work over the past four decades in procedures of behavioral control and modification has led the way to a fast-growing literature on the same subject.

The procedures described in the preceding chapters for dealing with stuttering follow the positivistic or behavioristic traditions. They are often contrasted, perhaps too harshly, with the "clinical" point of view. From this point of view, thoughts and feelings are considered to be valid and primary data. The clinician who espouses this philosophy accepts and deals with the phenomenological world—that is, he is interested in personal reports, introspection, conscious and unconscious processes, feelings, dreams, intentions, desires, and the individual attribution of meaning to experiences.

In stuttering, the clinical world has been one of common sense in principle and procedure, of a concern with psychodynamics, of trial and error thinking and action, of intuition or hunches, of focus on interpersonal relationships, and it has been a world in which a number of different approaches from different professional disciplines have been used. It is easy to see why the strict behaviorist, with his allegiance only to publically observable behavior, balks at the clinician's attention to the symbolic, the illogical, or to the total unity of a situation. For the behaviorist these things cannot be controlled or objectively measured. The clinician may regard his patient not simply as a reactor but as an active originating agent, so that it is little wonder that behaviorists have referred to such mentalisms as "the ghosts in the machine," although behavior modification procedures are being related more and more to the realm of private experience.

Some Observations on Behaviorism and Behaviorists

The following statements do not encompass all behavior modification viewpoints, but they do represent a great deal of the literature in this field. Similarly, the statements about operant procedures do not necessarily apply to the representatives of other behavioral viewpoints, including two-factor theorists.

1. It is usually assumed that behavior is learned through external reinforcement, specifically the procedures of classical or operant conditioning, or some combination of the two, such as a two-factor theory.

2. The focus is on publically observable behaviors, empirically derived concepts, and explicitly defined goals. This focus permits objectivity in measurement and specificity in method.

3. The technical terms used in behavioral analysis have a highly specific set of referents, so that workers trained in the same manner are able to communicate efficiently with one another.

4. Constitutional determiners, because they cannot be placed under experimental control, have been given little or no attention in the behavioral literature, although there has recently been a movement away from this trend. Similarly, "cause" or etiology in the usual sense is rarely focussed upon; stuttering is considered to be not the symptom, but the problem.

5. The effects of drugs or surgery, not being available to paramedical workers, are given little attention.

6. There is scant reference to assumptions or to theoretical issues; the term "behavioral analysis" is often used instead of behavioral theory. Skinner has pointed out (Psych. Review, LVII, 1950, 193-216) that when lawful changes in behavior are immediately observable to the senses, the taste or the need is lost for "imagined changes in some fanciful world of neurones, ideas, or intervening variables." Stress is always placed on the behavioral level of observation, on descriptions of observable relationships.

7. There has been little reference to theoretical inner-determining states, such as feelings, motivations, intuitions, or hopes, although recent work opposes this trend.

8. It is maintained that the only real channel open to behavioral change is environmental manipulation. Behavior, for the Skinnerian, is strengthened when it is followed by certain kinds of consequences. Specifically, responses that produce positive reinforcers or terminate negative ones are more likely to reoccur under similar conditions. This principle of operant conditioning is used clinically to strengthen desirable behaviors by arranging for them to be followed by reinforcing consequences. Therapy consists of arranging these contingencies. As Skinner said, "Any behavior which can be specified can be programmed." (Science, 16 Feb., 1968).

9. Statistics in any traditional sense, such as the use of group norms for example, are almost entirely disregarded. Skinner once said that a statistical program is not only unnecessary, "it is just wrong."

Behavior Modification and Clinicians

Behavioral analysis is popular now, and the success reported by its enthusiastic proponents will cause other speech clinicians to move toward one of two extremes: (1) they may get on the bandwagon, or (2) they may recoil from or denounce the system because of its scientific complexity, its apparently depersonalizing effects, or for some other reason. Those who denounce it may resent the idea of manipulating another's behavior, concluding that it runs against their nature. Others refuse to think of themselves as conveyors of

102

punishment, even though speech clinicians have for years, often without realizing it, used procedures that were truly punishing, as has been mentioned in several examples by Shames. Also, those who denounce it may miss the many techniques used in common by both the behaviorists and the more traditionally minded clinicians, as has been pointed out by Brutten.

Those who support the behavioral approach will not only recognize the similarities with older procedures; they will realize that the new approach has resulted in a systematization of practices that were formerly done in a less scientific, less experimentally productive, or less testable manner. Of course scientific rigor does not ensure practical application. Furthermore, behavioral programs always stand in danger of choosing trivial goals because it is the trivial goals that can be most readily translated into testable, operational statements.

Behavioral analysts are usually conspicuous for their enthusiasm, and one opponent suggested that the optimism came about because they were released from the anxiety of theory construction. To this, Skinner replied that there was a more obvious explanation: "Behavior analysis works." As "analysis," of course, it does work; at least it achieves the limited goals it sets for itself. Whether it works beyond analysis, whether behavioral modification works in any way that is both consistent and socially applicable to a considerable body of stutterers remains to be answered by the test of time.

We have, however, greeted the new behavioral techniques with considerable enthusiasm. Our profession has always been eager for new sources of assistance, and this is particularly true with regard to stuttering, which has frustrated our profession from its beginning. We must be careful that our eagerness for assistance does not lead to a premature and perhaps faulty application of behavioral methods. Clinicians who work with large numbers or groups of stutterers may need to be reminded that the reports on behavioral techniques have come largely from the laboratory and were derived primarily from experiments with single subjects. As a result, to apply these procedures to groups of stutterers or to stutterers in complex social settings, such as a classroom, requires extreme caution.

Clinicians who are enthusiastic about these new techniques should also realize that their belief in the goodness of the approach may, in itself, produce positive therapeutic results. There is a long and well-documented history of this phenomenon in research and therapy with drugs, and it is now recognized that one must wait until the enthusiasm, and the therapeutic success it generates, has died down before the true effectiveness of the new treatment can be properly assessed.

Some speech pathologists have voiced concern that some of our workers will use behavioral practices to satisfy their own need to dominate in an authoritarian role. There will be a small number of these, but this is no reason to indite the method. The clinician who must express his neurosis in his work will do so regardless of the therapeutic approach he employs.

Some clinicians will be enticed by the apparent simplicity of many reinforcement procedures; they will be disappointed. A proper understanding of these methods requires that one study and understand their basis or rationale. Thus, to use the techniques successfully, a substantial awareness of learning theory is called for, a content area insufficiently studied by most speech clinicians. Only with such an awareness can the curious clinician assess behavior modification in reasonable perspective. Even within the area of a particular view, for instance operant or two-factor approaches, he will find, as Brutten has mentioned, that the procedures cannot be applied in a simple, step-by-step manner. Clinicians who want to function in behavior modification as more than simply technicians will want to integrate a variety of therapeutic procedures and, from a deep sensitivity to the personal needs of the stutterers they serve, they will tailor a program of rehabilitation uniquely suited to the individual.

Behavioral research is not only difficult, it is expensive. Its heavy instrumentation squeezes the budget, both for initial purchase and maintenance. Although therapy procedures may call for less instrumentation than laboratory research, the practical aspects of acquiring, operating, and maintaining equipment are not a small consideration in behavioral methods.

Not only equipment, but materials too will be an important concern. *Individualized programs* are needed. There is no way, with behavioral or any other methodology, that a massed application of routinized procedures can successfully treat stutterers. When behavior is complex, and has taken a long time to be acquired, its modification is proportionately complex. Even in behavioral research, which is usually done with a single subject, the experimenter must observe and stipulate the behavior in detail and analyze it in terms of learning principles and mechanisms. So too, must the clinician examine, analyze, and specify the complex of stimuli affecting the stutterer. They may be produced by the stutterer's own behavior or by someone else's; they may involve language, general motor, or emotional behavior; they may include conditioned stimuli, conditioned reinforcers, and discriminative stimuli. Such a program is hardly simple.

Behavior Modification and the Stutterer

I have suggested that a clinician's way of regarding stuttering will reflect the way in which he regards man, and that clinicians will gravitate toward one of two basic views of human behavior. On the one hand, today's positivist, the behavioral engineer, believes that if he could control all of a person's stimulation, he would be able to predict and control his behavior, including speech. The humanist (I do not mean to imply that behaviorists are inhuman) believes that learning must be more than the shaping of behavior by authoritarian agents. Between these two positions, lies a range of philosophies about therapeutic intervention. This is the stutterer's inheritance of professional service. And he too will have proclivities toward one type of therapy or another. Some will want to be controlled by the clinician, and for them behavioral procedures will enable them to be dependent. Others will sense in the behavioral specificity and quantifiability a sureness, an accuracy, and an aura of certainty. They will be enthusiastic, and this enthusiasm will often contribute to success and recovery, at least in the early stages of therapy.

Other stutterers, however, will be resistant. As one high school stutterer stated: "Why am I being treated piecemeal? I am not made up of pieces. My speech is not a separate part of me . . . when I speak, all of me is affected, and when any part of me is affected my speech is affected too. I am not a mouthpiece separated from the body . . . and what's more, I hope that people look at me totally, not just my speech." This unknowing Gestaltist did not last long in one behavioral setting, in which his stuttering was regarded not as a symptom, but as the problem. Other stutterers will resist an aspect of therapy that Joseph Wolpe has called a hierarchy of systematic desensitization. In this procedure the subject is exposed, either in reality or in imagination, to a sequence of anxiety-laden tasks of increasing difficulty. In speech pathology, a sequence of speaking situations is arranged, from the easiest to the most difficult, the goal being to have the stutterer advance from one stage to the next most difficult one without losing the degree of control or fluency earlier attained. Many stutterers, however, want to achieve *full* fluency immediately and seem unable to relinquish the drive to do so. At the low end of the hierarchy, they perceive the gap between where they are and where they are going as immense, and they react with frustration, which decreases the probability of fluency. This resistance to moving slowly, step-by-step, through the desensitization hierarchy is a common hurdle to speech recovery.

Behavior Modification and Behavior

For years, some clinicians have spoken of "the need for stuttering." This implies or assumes that there is some underlying or internal cause, some drive or need-state, which creates tensions or disruptions in psychological equilibrium, which in turn are manifested in "surface" phenomena such as stuttering. From the point of view of these clinicians, attending only to the stuttering would be akin to placing a child with a fever in an ice box; the real problem would be missed. Instead, they would say, one must resolve the processes which underlie the symptom, and this will diminish also the outward manifestation, the stuttering. Any clinician who has this or a similar conception of stuttering will question the wisdom of strict behavior therapy. He will also ask whether the reduction of these symptoms without the removal of the underlying causes might not lead to the substitution of some other symptomatic behavior, which may turn out to be even more disastrous than stuttering. There are not enough data now to support this antibehavioral claim that symptom-substitution will occur if behavior modification is applied in such cases. Theoretically, however, the possibility exists, and more information about the ultimate limits of behavior modification's success is needed before firm conclusions, one way or the other, can be made.

The danger of symptom-substitution is only a portion of a much broader concern: By focussing only on publically observable behaviors, by being extremely cautious and conservative, by concentrating on accuracy and precision, the behavioral engineer may lose sight of total patterns of functioning; his genuine concern for the whole human may become smothered in a welter of detail. We do indeed behave "all of a piece," and we are perceived as such.

Behavioral practices, however, would appear to neglect the whole human. All behavioral practices rest on a foundation of either classical or operant conditioning, or some combination of both, as in Brutten's two-factor approach to stuttering. The phrase "two-factor" would apply, far from Brutten's wish, a rather simple framework for therapy. As Brutten himself has made abundantly clear, this is hardly the case. And in his chapter of this book, Brutten states that in order to modify *both* the emotional responses and the maladaptive adjustive responses *in an individual stutterer* requires great clinical skill. It also requires a sound knowledge of learning theory and suggests that a clinician without such knowledge should use caution. It may be that the human being is too complex for behavioral analysis.

For example, classical and operant conditioning are usually discussed as distinctly different entities, even so far as to require different terminologies. This suggests erroneously that there is no overlap between the two. Although indeed the responses involved may be different (motor in operant, visceral in classical conditioning), there can still be an overlap in the *functions* that a stimulus has: "A stimulus can have multiple functions both within one of the types of conditioning as well as between them. That is, one stimulus can be both a discriminative stimulus as well as a conditioned reinforcer." (Staats, A. W., *Learning, Language, and Cognition*, 1968, p. 90). The two-factor approach reminds us that Skinner's approach, especially in recent years, has been fundamentally a one-factor system, considered by many to be a serious weakness in light of the complexity of human behavior. A two-factor approach moves closer to a more totalistic view of stuttering behavior. For example, in the two-factor approach it is recognized that important responses can occur *covertly*, that is, they may not be accessible to immediate observation. Furthermore, these covert responses are often extremely complex and show their effects on other behaviors, including publically observable ones. Even this approach, however, may be oversimplified.

In the operant approach, the situation is even worse. The proponents of operant techniques of behavior modification have maintained that by manipulating the stimulus consequences of stutterers' instrumentally conditioned behaviors it is possible to reduce or extinguish them. But the use of response-contingent stimulation is not a simple matter. Which bits of behavior should be selected as targets from the wide repertoire presented by the stutterer? What sequence should the shaping steps be presented in? And how can programs be written that are appropriate to each individual? Even with a program uniquely constructed for a single individual, can one assume that it remains appropriate over time? But it is not just the operant approach that has difficult questions to answer. In terms of the two-factor process of deconditioning, for example, is it possible that long-standing, socially complex speaking situations can be deconditioned within a finite number of trials? And is it really feasible to arrange deconditioning consistently in natural settings?

We see, I think, that as a therapy program reflects a more comprehensive view of stuttering behavior, the clinical considerations themselves become more comprehensive and more complex. Compare this with a strictly operant view which focusses entirely on a miniature segment of stuttering behavior. The tallies of cumulative recorders will certainly be specific, probably too specific to represent a totally functioning organism. The tallies will reflect events which may be as much a function of the intermediary agent, the machine or the recording observer, as of the stutterer. For example, the most common acts selected by Skinner for observation were lever-pressing for the rat and disk-pecking for the pigeon. Although these responses were highly replicable and intersubjectively verifiable, they are certainly not properly representative samples of behavior for these two species; they do not reflect the wholistic functioning of either organism. In fact, the briefer or more specific the behavior samples taken, the more equivocal they become in terms of their significance for the understanding and modification of stuttering in any organismic sense.

The whole issue of reinforcements presents other problems to the practicing clinician unable to perform single-subject work in a highly controlled laboratory setting. What reinforcers are effective for a given stutterer? Just because a clinician regards a reinforcer as appropriate does that mean a stutterer will react to it in the same way? Is it not possible that a given reinforcer will vary in its "degree of goodness" over time. Certainly it will vary over subjects. Will the goodness of a reinforcer not also vary depending on the setting? Will there not, in fact, be a hierarchy of reinforcers, and will not this hierarchy too be in a constant state of flux? How also can we define the response that is to be reinforced? Isn't it more than the simple contraction of a muscle-group? When stutterers are reinforced for speaking in a class or other group, they have usually emitted a wide variety of responses; which ones were reinforced?

Sometimes clinicians use "primary" reinforcers, for example food, particularly with nonverbal children. But with stutterers the reinforcements are more often conditioned ones, and these are usually words, such as "good," "fine," or "good job." But these words have their own conditioning history, varying of course from one individual to the next. They have built up, through their association with primary or other reinforcers, a certain effectiveness of function. But what of the stutterers who have heard these words from people they dislike? We all know people at whose compliments we scoff. Also, even effective conditioned reinforcers lose their effectiveness if they occur too often in the absence of more primary reinforcement. The clinician who uses words of praise too often will eventually find them ineffective.

All therapists are familiar with the difficulty of getting behaviors that were acquired in the clinic to generalize to more natural social settings. It is one thing to decide what behavior is to be reinforced and what behavior is not in a highly controlled behavior modification structure. But in a group speaking situation, the determination of which responses are occurring as efficient operants is another matter. How, in a rapidly changing social situation, is the stutterer's repertoire of behavior to be segmentalized into responses? And what events are reinforcers? These are not impossible problems to solve, but they are difficult, and they are crucial to a clinician trying to apply behavior modification to ordinary life situations.

In order to achieve complete carry-over, it is necessary to set up appropriate reinforcers in the stutterer's everyday world. This means that others, such as parents and teachers, must be trained to be effective sources of reinforcement to the stutterer. This presents large practical problems. In addition to the problems of time and expense involved whenever the clinician participates with the stutterer in these transitional activities, the people who are being trained as sources of reinforcement find it quite a challenge to administer reinforcement to a single individual in a group situation such as a classroom. And of course, one always wonders whether the stutterer will eventually come to exercise whatever improved behavior he has developed on his own, in the absence of external social reinforcement. Such a question brings us back, of course, to the inner motivation of the individual. In the fully functioning person, reinforcement works primarily in a prospective sense; that is, it is usually from the *recognition* of consequences, not from the consequences themselves, that the human being ties his history to the future. It is by knowing what will happen, not what has happened, that the human being avoids pain and seeks pleasure, on condition, of course, that he is interested in doing so and judges it worthwhile.

Conclusion

As our profession strives, perhaps too diligently, to become a hard-core scientific discipline, we can be sure that a great deal of attention will be directed to the components of human functioning. After all, the behavior of the total organism must, somehow, emanate from and be a product of these components, their relationship to one another, and the processes and principles according to which they occur. We do not yet know if it is possible, or indeed ever will be, to arrange all these components into a relationship that is relevant to the human being in his world rather than merely in the laboratory.

It is difficult not to study what is immediately available and to study what actually *is*. It is simply not enough to know how man reacts; we must also know how he feels and how he regards his world and himself. The clinician's job must be more than simply describing and shaping stutterers; it should be to experience and understand them, and to help them chart the course of their own becoming.

An Evaluation of Behavior Modification in the Treatment of Stuttering

RICHARD M. BOEHMLER, Ph.D.

Perhaps the most relevant fact about stuttering, from the clinician's point of view, is that it is a disruption of communication. Therefore, in order to understand what stuttering is and in order to know how to treat it, the clinician must understand how the disorder of stuttering is related to each of the many aspects of communication: concept-formation, choice-making, language acquisition, voice and articulation production, prosody patterns, communication feedback systems, fluency breakdown, and others. We must bear in mind the complexity of the disorder and the correspondingly broad responsibility of the clinician as we evaluate the behavioral approaches to the treatment of stuttering. There are three areas in which the behavioral approaches cause concern: (1) a definition of stuttering suitable for use by the clinician has not been provided, (2) measurement techniques are not adequate to the task suggested, and (3) behavioral science has not yet reached a level of sophistication sufficient to handle the complicated problem of stuttering.

A Clinical Definition of Stuttering

The behavioral approaches set forth in this book are a great help to the clinician in furthering his understanding of stuttering, but they fail to assist him in discharging some of his most important clinical responsibilities. The most basic of these responsibilities is diagnosis—identifying the client who is a stutterer and identifying a given behavior as stuttering. This process of identification hinges directly on the clinician's or the clinic's definition of stuttering.

The behaviorist may legitimately limit himself to dealing with observable, repeatable, measurable patterns of behavior. It is appropriate and useful to expand our knowledge by accumulating data through this approach. We must, however, realize that there are practical limitations to applying these data in the clinic. First, the behavioral experimenter deals largely, in some cases exclusively, with those behaviors that are most readily observed—lip protrusion, eye-blinking, vocal repetitions—and often ignores the less observable behaviors—vocalis muscle contractions, diaphragm movement, velopharyngeal closure, and so on. Behaviors that are more difficult to observe are not even considered, and this includes the infinitesimal responses of the neurones in the central nervous system.

The clinician recognizes that the degree to which a specific

111

behavior is relevant to a communication disorder does not depend only upon the observability of that behavior. Many behaviors that are not readily observable are clinically vital. The clinician, however, must determine how important a given behavior is in terms of how seriously it impairs communication. To make this determination, a clinician must know about the voice quality, temporal patterns, and pitch patterns in relation to the neighboring sounds and syllables before he knows if the disfluency disrupted communication or not. For example, a repetition containing only two units produced at the same rate, pitch, and intensity as the surrounding sounds or syllables might be totally unnoticed in a given communication situation and consequently would not be significant. The same repetition, however, might require serious consideration if it were noxious to the speaker or to a listener. Behaviorists have customarily been concerned only with whether or not a behavior was observable, not with its importance as a disruptor of communication.

The strict behaviorists miss much that is useful to a deep understanding of stuttering when they refuse to consider the largely unobservable or inferred behaviors. For example, many clinicians feel that the stutterer's self-image is an important aspect of the problem, and when modifying the behavior of a stutterer these clinicians will want to take the stutterer's self-image into account. Obviously, one's self-image is not directly observable. At best, we infer its nature by direct measurement. And, since it is not directly observable, it is not discussed or studied by the usual behaviorist. For the clinician who is concerned with nonobservables, this is a serious omission. For them, stuttering involves the private thoughts of the individual as well as his overt speaking behavior.

Another example of nonobservable behavior considered important by many, is the behavior involved in making decisions. Although we can observe the behavior resulting from the decision-making, we cannot observe the process itself. But there are many clinicians who feel that decision-making is an important aspect of stuttering. They are concerned with the client's decision to use a particular avoidance pattern, to speak or to remain silent, to attend a therapy session or not, and so on. These clinicians, as part of therapy, try to influence the stutterer's decision-making; they use hypnosis or suggestion, positive identification, and hope as some of the clinical tools used to modify the decision-making process.

In general terms, the behaviorists define stuttering in a way that is more restrictive than most of the definitions used in clinical situations. As a result, the clinician must be very cautious in applying the behaviorist's findings.

Operant Conditioning

The proponents of operant conditioning do not adequately define what they mean by stuttering, nor do they speculate on the significance of the behaviors they manipulate to the subject's total communication pattern. A researcher can arbitrarily designate "sound or word repetitions and short, jerky holding and releasing of the breath" (Martin, 1968) as stuttering, and proceed to manipulate these behaviors. But the clinician cannot be so arbitrary with his clients. He must know first what part these behaviors play in the total communication process and second the relative significance of these behaviors to other behaviors (often less observable) exhibited by the client before he can decide whether it is *desirable* to manipulate them. Operant researchers often imply that other behaviors exist that are relevant to the communication process, but they frequently leave their identity a mystery. Martin, for example, writes (1968, p. 342.) " . . . certain of the overt nonfluent or struggle behaviors emitted *during stuttering* are susceptible to experimental manipulation in much the same way as are other operant behaviors" (italics mine). Martin does not state the nature of *the stuttering* during which nonfluent or struggle behaviors occur. He states that stuttering[1] (nonfluent or struggle behaviors) occurs "during" stuttering.[2] Stuttering[2] is left undefined.

Is stuttering[2], in this example, less desirable than stuttering[1]? Perhaps stuttering[3] (say, prolongations) is more desirable than either stuttering[1] or stuttering[2]. Perhaps prolongations, repetitions, and knee-slapping are all undesirable, or perhaps they are all desirable for a particular client at a particular stage in his language development. Operant conditioning *principles* do not answer these questions. But *clinicians,* including those who use operant conditioning, should.

Goldiamond (1968, pg. 349-407) implies that prolongations are not an example of stuttering behavior. But many speakers and their audiences see *prolongations* as "stuttering," and many clinicians, therefore, realize that some of their clients have to modify this behavior as well as repetitions, etc. Regardless of which is the correct definition, the clinician must apply Goldiamond's results and conclusions with extreme caution if his concept of stuttering differs from that implied by Goldiamond.

One must be particularly cautious when a writer makes a generalization in which the term *stuttering* is included. In his diagram (Figure 1, p. 21), Shames makes such a generalization. By using the term *stuttering responses,* Shames implies that all stuttering responses are operants. The clinician should know that the word *stuttering,* as he might use it with a specific client, may not refer to the same behaviors that Shames includes in Figure 1. In short, Shames, and others, have generalized about "stuttering behavior," without defining the referents for the term.

Shames has also discussed the use of delayed auditory feedback as a clinical tool. In this approach, the DAF is used to produce in the stutterer a "prolonging type of speech." Many clinicians, however, believe that under certain circumstance prolongations are a type of stuttering behavior, and for them, delayed auditory feedback is an effective way to teach a client to stutter. Shames indicates, however, that the "prolonging type of speech" is "nonstuttering." He thus sets forth an arbitrary definition of stuttering, and he assumes that culturally it is more desirable to prolong than to repeat. The opposite point of view, however, is equally tenable, particularly when the repetitions are relaxed, are in the same rhythm pattern as other syllables, and contain only one or two oscillations. A prolongation, however, may be highly noxious to the speaker or his listeners since it constitutes an abrupt change in the rhythm pattern, even when such prolongations occur at the low rate of one per hour.

The clinician who works with the elementary school stutterer should take an even closer look at Shames' stuttering behavior programs. Two of these programs are set forth. One is designed for those stutterers who exhibit overt struggle behaviors to the extent that communication is severely impaired. The second program is designed for the stutterer whose primary disorder is in the thematic content of his language. Although Shames indicates that operant programs need not be limited to these persons, the limitations of these programs should not be taken lightly. It is a fact that the behavior patterns of most stutterers seen by the elementary school clinician do not fit either of Shames' descriptions. Most firstgraders who have a high number of syllable repetitions do not exhibit overt struggle behavior to the extent that communication is severely impaired; they talk freely, communicate with relative effectiveness, and have little or no concern about stuttering (Bloodstein, *JSHD*, XXV and XXVI).

It is often a mistake in judgment to assume that children with frequent repetitions but without struggle or awareness do not have a communication problem. These behavioral patterns are often the first signs that the development of fluency patterns may be taking a potentially dangerous path. The clinician must be certain that the child is not developing in an undesirable direction, and he must take appropriate action if this is what is happening. The responsible clinician cannot wait to see which children develop struggle and avoidance and then provide therapy. He cannot afford to ignore these children just because Shames and others have not published an operant program for this type of client.

It would be unfair to leave this discussion of operant conditioning and the definition of stuttering without acknowledging the significant contributions the operant approach has made to the management of behavioral patterns in certain clients. For example, a child who has highly disfluent speech which is also related to inadequate language formulation might profit from an operant program which is designed to increase those articulatory-phonation patterns which occur when language formulation is complete and adequate and which reduces those that occur when language

114

formulation is incomplete or inadequate. The clinician cannot afford to ignore these children or fail to treat their basic communication problem just because an operant program has not yet been published for their particular need.

We may conclude then that operant conditioning is useful to the clinician, but the definition of what stuttering is and the decision as to what part of it should be modified requires more information than the current proponents of operant conditioning have provided.

The Two-Factor Theory

Stuttering is a term used by speech clinicians to refer to a number of different behavioral patterns. The term is useful as a label for the total concept which includes all of these different behavioral patterns. When, however, the term is used to refer to only one of these patterns, then much of what is significant to the total problem is omitted from discussion. The two-factor theory of stuttering makes this error. Specifically, it fails to include a number of significant sources of fluency disintegration by restricting its definition of stuttering severely.

According to the two-factor theory, stuttering is defined as "involuntary fluency failures that result from classically conditioned negative emotion." All other forms of fluency failure are excluded from the definition and are considered to be something other than stuttering. This is a vast oversimplification of the many diverse patterns that have been observed to occur during the development of stuttering. For example, a pre-school child may exhibit a number of unemotional syllable repetitions while talking to his mother. Despite the fact that these syllable repetitions were not associated with negative emotion, conditioned or unconditioned, they may easily interfere with the child's communication and may have been extremely important in the development of stuttering. Such repetitions need our professional attention, but they are omitted from the definition of stuttering used in the two-factor theory.

The two-factor theory discusses at some length those behaviors that are not so closely associated with the speaking mechanism. These behaviors, which have been called "struggle reactions," or "secondary behaviors," are referred to in the two-factor theory as "instrumentally conditioned coping behaviors." They are theorized to occur when the stutterer attempts to escape or avoid the fluency failures precipitated by classically conditioned negative emotion. These instrumentally conditioned behaviors, however, are not considered by the two-factor theory to be stuttering behaviors. Here again, many speech clinicians consider these behaviors as an important aspect of the total communication problem. The fact that the two-factor theorists have outlined a program of therapy for these instrumentally conditioned behaviors serves only to make their definitional posture seem less consistent—if one is going to treat stutterers for these behaviors, surely the behaviors should be considered as part of the disorder called stuttering. Again, the definitions used in the two-factor theory seem to oversimplify the concept of stuttering.

It is worth pointing out that the instrumentally conditioned coping behaviors do not occur only in response to "involuntary fluency failures that result from classically conditioned negative emotion," as the two-factor theory would have us believe. They can also occur in response to or in anticipation of fluency breakdown resulting from language formulation inadequacies or from inadequate neuromuscular patterns for articulation. Regardless of the source of the breakdown, the fluency failure can become a noxious stimulus for the speaker so that avoidance and escaping behavior are likely to follow. Such fluency breakdowns, from sources other than classically conditioned negative emotion, may be highly significant aspects of the communication disorder we call stuttering. But the two-factor theory excludes them from consideration.

In conclusion, it is apparent that the two-factor theory will "fit" the behavioral patterns of a number of our clients, but because it excludes a number of important features of stuttering from its definition, it would also exclude a number of clients whom we must serve. This is particularly true of our young clients, who we see because of stuttering but who are not "stuttering" according to the two-factor theory. Furthermore, considering any given client, the two-factor theory would exclude from the category of stuttering behaviors many behaviors that most speech clinicians would consider stuttering behaviors. As clinicians, we cannot responsibly limit ourselves to such a highly restrictive definition of stuttering.

As clinicians, we should apply and make use of the legitimate contributions of behaviorism—both the operant and two-factor versions—and it is useful to translate our own individual concepts of stuttering into behavioral terminology. But that does not mean that we must change our concept of stuttering, either by focussing on behaviors that are most readily observable or by abandoning our use of the term *stuttering* as a label for a broad abstraction or concept and restricting its use to refer to certain specific behaviors which are only a part of the total disorder.

The Measurement of Stuttering

As we said above, the behaviorists deal with those behaviors that are observable. The purpose of restricting one's activities to observable behaviors is to restrict consideration only to those behaviors that are operationally measurable. The reliability thus obtained is obviously an advantage for the experimenter, but there is also a corresponding danger for the clinician. The clinician who restricts himself to strictly observable behaviors and avoids dealing with the less observable, less measurable behaviors will necessarily

116

have to exclude from consideration how relevant those behaviors are to the stuttering problem. Behaviorism should not teach the clinician what to measure—it should teach him how to measure better the behaviors he is concerned with.

Measurement and the Operant Approach

Currently, the behaviorists are dealing with repetitions, prolongations, eye-blinks, lip-protrusions, and so on, in their research on stuttering. But many clinicians consider other behaviors, less observable and less measurable, as a significant aspect of the problem. Can a behavioral approach be applied, for example, to the process of decision-making, to the stutterer's mental set, to articulatory motor planning, to perfectionism? The answer to this question may well be yes, but few of the necessary programs have yet been devised.

Consider, as an example, the process of decision-making in the stutterer. Suppose that a stutterer has learned a particular avoidance pattern over the years. In therapy he has also learned an alternate, specific, but more adaptive behavioral pattern. The second pattern has proven to be a desirable step toward better communication. Regardless of the extent to which the stutterer has learned these two response patterns, provided he has reached a certain minimal level, he can choose one pattern over the other when the time comes. If the avoidance pattern were to occur solely because of the relative strengths of the two motor habits, it would probably be impossible to condition the stutterer to substitute a new habit for the old one, since the old one had been reinforced daily for many years. Therefore, conscious decision-making is an important aspect in the clinical management of stutterers.

How, within the system of behaviorism, do we define "conscious decision-making" and how do we apply operant techniques to increase its occurrence? We cannot measure it with the careful precision that the behaviorists have measured eyeblinks. We might, however, be able to measure such an unobservable entity by inferring its presence from some other, more readily observable, behavior. For example, the making of a decision requires time, so that we might assume, when there is a delayed reaction, that decision-making was taking place. We could even go one step further and use operant techniques to condition the occurrence of these delayed reactions so that they occurred more frequently, but could we be certain that we had conditioned the *decision-making* to occur more frequently?

Many clinicians want to deal with behavior patterns that are even less observable than decision-making. As a clinician I have been impressed with the importance of a client's tendency to use a wide variety of behaviors but which are still restricted or stereotyped in

117

their function. This general tendency might be identified as a mental set; either to try new and different solutions to the problem or to repeat, almost compulsively, an old and tried selection of responses. The adult stutterer can learn to recognize such a set and from it to predict the likelihood of his employing or not employing a whole pattern of behaviors, such as a therapy program. Clients can learn to recognize and discriminate this set without necessarily having to experience communication. They can tell you which side of the therapy bed they got up on. All clinicians, including those using operant approaches, use a number of clinical tools to influence this mental set: suggestion or hypnosis, positive identification with the clinician, and a promise of improvement are frequently used.

We could describe these mental sets in terms of the behaviors they generate. When the stutterer uses the desirable set he attends therapy and consciously chooses to use the behavior patterns that lead to effective communication. We could then set up a list of different behavioral patterns from which the clinician could infer the condition which he calls mental set. We could then set about writing a program for manipulating these patterns. We could never be certain that we were manipulating mental set, but recognizing this, we might be inclined to try harder. This kind of a program, however, is vastly more complicated than any of the programs proposed by operant clinicians. Such a program would deal not just with one behavior pattern but with a whole complexity of behaviors. As clinicians we apparently feel that these more abstract behavior complexes are important, otherwise we would not use such terms as "mental set." Since operant conditioning has been shown to be an effective tool for managing behavior, it behooves us to define these terms in specific enough behaviorial language that operant conditioning can be used. The question is, can such a reduction of an abstract behavioral complex into specific behavioral terms be made without serious loss? From a behaviorist's point of view, this is an empirical question which is testable. The need to improve our services to the client is certainly worth the risk of trying such new approaches.

The Two-Factor Theory and the Measurement of Stuttering

The two-factor theory of stuttering distinguishes between two types of behavior—instrumentally conditioned coping responses and fluency failures that result from classically conditioned negative emotion. Of the two types of behavior, the measurement of fluency disintegration presents the larger challenge to the clinician. In this section we will suggest: (1) that fluency failures cannot be readily identified, (2) that the negative stimuli theorized to precipitate them are also difficult to identify, and (3) that the two-factor theory fails to distinguish, in any operational way, between stutterers and nonstutterers.

118

Within the two-factor theory, it is necessary to distinguish fluency disintegration that results from negative emotion from all other forms of fluency disintegration (Brutten and Shoemaker, 1967, p. 42). We do not yet have the skill necessary to make this distinction, although it may be that this skill will eventually be developed. A number of difficulties make it impossible at the present time to make this distinction which is so vital to the two-factor theory. First of all, the degree of emotional response necessary to interfere with normal articulatory movements is relatively small. For example, normal patterns of phonation are disintegrated by a relatively small amount of glottal tension. These breakdowns are often exceedingly difficult to detect, either by the clinician or by the stutterer himself. Most adult stutterers who have had years of experience with fluency failure, are unable to identify the locus of any particular fluency disintegration. Yet the two-factor theory assumes that we will be able not only to locate them but to separate them into breakdowns that result from classically conditioned negative emotion and breakdowns that result from all other causes.

The second problem with the two-factor theory concerns the identification of the noxious stimuli that precipitate fluency failure. It is frequently difficult to determine if an organism has even perceived a change in ongoing environmental energy, at least without referring to reports by the subject. It is even more difficult to determine whether a stimulus, assuming that it was perceived, was noxious to the organism. When, in the course of a conversation, does an /s/ become noxious to a stutterer? There may be ways of answering this question, but, with stutterers, more often than not, it is not the act of articulating the /s/, nor the acoustical feedback of articulating the /s/, but the thinking of the /s/ that is noxious to the stutterer. No behavioral approach can adequately deal with such internal stimuli. Furthermore, it is entirely possible that such an internal stimulus could be noxious to the stutterer without his even having been aware that the stimulus occurred. As a result, we find that behaviorists tend to deal with those stimuli which the stutterer is aware of, which he realizes are noxious, and which he reports to us. Behaviorists usually disregard those stimuli that are unconscious, the noxiousness of which is not realized, or which are so fleeting that they are not reported. These difficulties apply to the adult stutterer, but for the young stutterer, whose awareness of stimulation and of noxiousness is on a much lower level, the difficulties are much more profound. Another difficulty related to the measurement of noxious stimulation is that by requesting a stutterer to tell us about the stimuli that he finds noxious, we heighten his awareness of them. In some cases we may create awareness where formerly there was none. As clinicians, we must be wary of the consequences of heightening such awareness, particularly in the beginning stutterer.

The third difficulty with the two-factor theory is that it fails to distinguish between stutterers and nonstutterers. This is true because it is necessary, in order to make the distinction, to artificially dichotomize a continuum. Brutten and Shoemaker write:

> The term stuttering should be applied by pathologists only when the disruptions of speech fluency significantly exceed the individual's usual level of disfluency, when the fluency failures are chronic rather than sporadic in their presence, and when the disorganizations are dependent upon conditioned negative emotion whose very existence and magnitude is inappropriate to the stimulus situation.

The terms "significantly exceed," "chronic rather than sporadic," "appropriate" and "inappropriate," represent continua, and in order to distinguish stuttering from nonstuttering it is necessary to divide these continua at a particular point. Of course, it is impossible to divide continua at a particular point with any degree of reliability, and it would be unfair to suggest that Brutten and Shoemaker have implied that this is not the case. But it is questionable whether one can even approximate such a division with the measurement tools now in hand. And when even the approximation of such a division is impossible, it is fair to conclude that Brutten and Shoemaker's theory fails to distinguish between stutterers and nonstutterers, at least in light of our current measurement skills. Yet they imply that such a distinction should be made. They indicate that "stuttering" should be applied only to a portion of the behavioral continuum. Clinically, it is more valid not to divide the fluency continuum into such a dichotomy. This is not only a problem of measurement but a basic issue concerning application of measurement tools.

Thus, the two-factor theory raises serious measurement problems with regard to (1) distinguishing between different types of fluency disintegration, (2) identifying the stimuli that precipitate fluency disintegration, and (3) dichotomizing the stuttering-nonstuttering continuum.

The Limited Application of Behaviorism to Stuttering

Most behaviorists will agree that the present level of information about learning is extremely low, and most of them preface their discussions with an apology to this effect. Behaviorism is an infant science. It has few laws and only slightly more principles. The field should not be criticized, however, for its youth. Presumably it will grow up. One must, however, question the application of such an infant discipline to areas of extreme complexity in which the lives of human beings are affected. As clinicians, can we simultaneously apply these highly simple behavioral principles to our complicated patients and retain our clinical competence?

120

A number of studies suggest that certain stuttering behaviors can be reduced in frequency by the use of punishment. The subject, however, is more complicated than this—he contains more than just these responses. And, when punishment is used, will it not automatically cause those behaviors that are being punished to become noxious stimuli to the subject? Might not the noxious stimulation of punishment produce other behaviors equally or even more undesirable than those being reduced? So many events take place in a client at any given time, that we may do more harm than good by isolating a few individual responses and working with them alone without considering the consequences of our actions to other behaviors.

The application of behavioral principles to stuttering may also be limited because our knowledge of stuttering itself is highly limited. One of the more easily defined bits of behavior involved in stuttering is the syllable repetition, and much of the behavioral experimentation has been done with this response. Unfortunately, we know very little about this form of behavior. The occurrence of repetitions in the speech of adults and children has been investigated only cursorily and little is known about them. We do not know why the repetitions of some individuals are slow and relaxed while those of others are rapid and tense. We do not know why most adults occasionally repeat a sound once or twice at a normal articulatory rate with little or no awareness on their part and get by with little listener reaction. We do not know how these repetitions differ from the rapid, jerky repetitions which other individuals produce. The repetition of the first sound of a word does not appear to be the same behavior as a repetition of a schwa before a word. It seems clear that we do not have enough data on repetitions. And yet the behaviorists apply their principles to this behavior. It seems clear that we do not know enough even about repetitions alone to apply the oversimplified principles of behaviorism to those repetitions. Much less should we apply these oversimplified principles to stuttering behaviors of which repetitions are but one example. The danger of applying overly simple principles to complicated human beings applies equally to the operant and two-factor approaches.

Summary

We have examined in this chapter the behavioral approaches to the treatment of stuttering, and we have found the following shortcomings in their analysis:

1. The behavioral approaches fail to define stuttering in a manner that is usable by the clinician.

2. The behavioral approaches fail to describe stuttering in a way that permits it to be measured adequately.

3. The behavioral approaches fail to provide an analysis of stuttering that is equal to its subtleties and complexities.

References

Goldiamond, I., *Stuttering and Fluency as Manipulatable Operant Response Classes."* in Sloane, A. W., and MacAuley, B. D. (Eds), *Operant Procedures in Remedial Speech and Language Training.* Boston: Houghton Mifflin, 1968.

Martin, R., "The Experimental Manipulation of Stuttering Behavior," in Sloane, A. W., and MacAuley, B. D., (Eds.), *Operant Procedures in Remedial Speech and Language Training.* Boston: Houghton Mifflin, 1968.

Reflections on the Behavioral Modification of Stuttering

JOSEPH G. SHEEHAN, Ph. D.

One of the salient features of stuttering as contrasted with other disorders, is that its behavior is outwardly expressed and directly observable and seems to follow principles of learning. The therapies which have been clinically derived for stuttering have been based largely upon direct behavioral methods. It is therefore not surprising that stuttering should have become a favorite target of the new army of behavior therapists and operant conditioners. Some members of this army seem to be marching without any map of the territory of the disorder called stuttering, and without any awareness of its complexities. Where are they heading?

This chapter is largely an evaluation and commentary on behavior modification in general and operant conditioning specifically, as these approaches might be and have been applied to stuttering. With the direct modification of behavior as a method, either in psychotherapy or in stuttering therapy, we are in agreement. We modify stuttering largely through the selective reinforcement of some responses, and the selective nonreinforcement of others.

Though we have no basic quarrel with therapies based upon the direct modification of behavior, we are quite concerned with the manner in which behavior therapy techniques in general and operant conditioning methods in particular have been applied to stuttering thus far.

A Paradoxical Disorder

Stuttering is full of paradoxes. Why should anyone have difficulty speaking in this glib world, when so much of what is said is banal and useless? Why should children continue to stutter when the behavior is apparently more punished than rewarded? Why do some stutterers recover spontaneously? Why should anyone stutter most when he is trying hardest not to? Why does one child stutter under pressure when another, equally pressured, does not? Why does stuttering behavior often decrease when it is treated permissively but increase with social penalty?

There are innumerable amateur therapists and theorists who have answers to these questions. Stutterers quickly learn that everyone offers advice, and the methods suggested are so common that a folklore of stuttering has developed. "Take a deep breath,"

123

"Slow down," "Relax," "Think before you speak," are the most popular. Stutterers learn that everyone thinks he can cure stuttering but that nobody really can. Therapy comes easy, but the therapists can't be trusted. Advice costs nothing, and it may be worth less.

Stuttering Therapy: Basic Operations

Historically, many stuttering therapies go back to Knight Dunlap (1931) and the concept of negative practice. The basic idea was that habits may be broken by practicing them voluntarily. Dunlap felt that there was one thing we could always ask a stutterer to do—he could stutter! Dunlap evolved an entire therapy on the technique of having the client consciously duplicate the true stuttering pattern as closely as possible.

At the University of Iowa, a number of clinicians, especially Van Riper and Johnson, adapted negative practice into various forms. Sometimes, they duplicated the primary symptoms of stuttering (repetition and prolongation), rather than the full pattern (including the secondary behaviors), as in the Dunlap method. Voluntary syllable repetition came to be known as "the bounce," and many stutterers, including Johnson himself, bounced their way through many syllabic years. Van Riper introduced the "stop-go," based on the preparatory set principle, in which the stutterer used the signal of expected stuttering to get set and the feeling of the block, which was presumably neurological, to "go" on the rest of the word. Subsequent research, however, suggested that the neurological block was not a valid concept, although many stutterers who believed it used Van Riper's technique with reasonable success. Later, however, Van Riper replaced it with more advanced methods.

Another variation on negative practice was refined by Sheehan. Called "the slide," this technique was to be used primarily on nonfeared words. The stutterer prolonged slightly the initial sound and the transition to the rest of the word, keeping the release as smooth and gradual as possible and maintaining sound throughout. This technique was found to be superior to the bounce and to the Dunlap method of exact duplication, and, in explanation for this success we suggested:

It is quite likely that the stutterer in attempting to hit a feared word, shows some of the same behavior as the hunter who begins to pull the trigger before he has fully aimed. The hunter who jerks and startles on his gun before he is able to press the trigger is taught to *squeeze the trigger slowly.* When the trigger is squeezed rather than jerked, the proprioceptive cues mediating the startle response are not present, and the hunter is able to hit his target. Similarly, when the stutterer tries to jerk out the feared word, the maladaptive anticipatory startle responses prevent success. But when he hits the

124

word gradually with a sliding speech attempt (or slows down the rate of stuttering), he prevents the internal cues which set off the startle reaction. Hence this type of disruption occurs less frequently when the slide is used (Sheehan and Voas, 1957).

Avoidance Versus Acceptance

Stuttering therapies are easily divisible into two classes, one based on avoidance and one based on acceptance. The archaic therapies which aimed at immediate fluency, through the use of devices to prevent the occurrence of stuttering, are of the avoidance type. Demosthenes' pebbles, Itard's fork, and recent attempts to employ masking noise or delayed speech feedback fall into this category. Also in this category are more sophisticated attempts to produce fluency through increased self-confidence, or suggestion. By whatever method it was produced, fluency in this approach is then nurtured in the hope that it will spread from the rather special circumstances that produced it to more general situations throughout life. In this approach, it is vital that stuttering be prevented from occurring. Should the stutterer experience failure, he must begin again, or go back to an earlier point in the sequence of procedures. Unfortunately, most of the operant techniques suggested to date follow this older school.

The other approach, which is based on the acceptance of stuttering, is derived from the view that stuttering is a conflict, a kind of vicious circle. If the stutterer will, for a while, accept himself as a stutterer, he can reduce the conflict and become fluent. Avoidance is therefore reduced, while at the same time the stuttering pattern is modified into a simpler form.

Careful self-observation and continual monitoring can bring about attitudinal and behavioral changes automatically. Group therapy with other stutterers, sometimes including psychotherapy, facilitates self-awareness. Increased fluency then becomes a by-product of the stutterer's increased self-acceptance. This approach has been spelled out in detail in *Stuttering: Research and Therapy* (Sheehan, 1970) and in other writings. Van Riper's techniques, which are quite different from the methods just outlined, may also be considered as falling into the category of therapies in which stuttering is accepted.

Stuttering as a False-Role Disorder

Stuttering may be viewed as a false-role disorder, a self-role conflict expressed in competing approach and avoidance tendencies toward the act of speaking. Stuttering frequently occurs as a result of efforts to prevent its occurrence. Many of the stutterer's behaviors would not be necessary if he did not try to deny or prevent their occurrence.

125

If we placed a two-by-four flat on the floor of a room, nearly anyone could walk along it without stepping off. But if we placed the same plank between two buildings or across a chasm, the probability of falling would be vastly increased by the danger. Efforts to avoid a consequence can sometimes produce it. The stutterer who tries to be perfectly fluent increases the conflict and consequently the likelihood of fluency disruption.

Stuttering as Learned Behavior

There is impressive evidence that much of what we observe as stuttering is accountable as learned behavior. Apparently, the stutterer's emotional pattern is classically conditioned, and his stuttering pattern is instrumentally conditioned.

Behavior is determined by its consequences. Reward or punishment obviously influence behavior, although we do not always know how they work. Patterns of punishment and reinforcement can be extremely complicated and stuttering appears to reflect a complex set of behaviors. Clinicians tend to attribute this complexity to individual psychodynamics; behavior therapists cover it by the equally vague term "reinforcement history."

Often omitted from consideration of reward and punishment is the question of how soon after the behavior they occur. Immediate consequences may have quite a different effect from long-range consequences. For example, rewards for fluently spoken words given out during an experimental session may have no effect at all on the future probability of stuttering under the very different stimulus conditions outside the laboratory. To make stutterers fluent in a sheltered environment is as meaningless as it is easy. The perceptive clinician soon learns what nearly every stutterer knows—that fluent intervals lead neither to a reduction of fear nor to a solution of the problem.

Behavior Modification

The term behavior modification may be used to include all approaches to clinical problems based on information derived from experiments on learning and conditioning. Within this definition, operant conditioning is just one type of behavior modification. The "negative practice" techniques of Dunlap, mentioned earlier, would also be an early type of behavior modification. Similarly, the techniques developed by Van Riper and others in our field, although not usually given such recognition, should also be considered as behavior modification.

Many of the most avid behavior modification advocates tend confusingly to use the term *behavior modification* as synonymous with operant conditioning. Operant conditioning, however, is just one type of behavior modification.

The Social Reinforcement of Fluency

Johnson and others showed many years ago that most stutterers speak most of their words fluently. Consequently, fluency, in stutterers, has already been subjected to a vast amount of positive reinforcement. It could even be argued that for a stutterer the social consequences of speaking a word fluently are even more strongly reinforced than for a normal speaker. Can the operant conditioners hope to do better? Can "laboratory" (a prestige word operant conditioners have themselves programmed to employ at every opportunity) manipulations of masking and delayed side-tone effects really accomplish what a lifetime of positive social reinforcement has failed to accomplish?

No, the problem lies elsewhere. It is our view that stuttering is learned in response to punishment and is perpetuated in most stutterers by the anticipation of further punishment. Therefore, the stutterer does not need reinforcement for fluent words. He can, however, be helped to modify his avoidance reactions through the use of reinforcement and nonreinforcement. He can break out of the vicious circle. Though it isn't easy, there's nothing very mysterious about it. On his part, it calls for courage; on the part of the clinician, it calls for sensitivity, imagination, and skill. This therapy aims at decreasing the penalty for stuttering and reducing the stutterer's tendency to hold back. It gives the stutterer a way of coping with fear and with moments of stuttering.

Ryan has focused more on stuttering therapy techniques in this book than on the simple reinforcement of fluent speech. Although the operant language in which it is presented may seriously retard its assimilation by many therapists, it may be that further development of Ryan's type of operant programming will lead to more systematic application of reinforcement principles where they can do some good.

Furthermore, the use of a reinforcement technique does not preclude the consideration of a broader psychotherapeutic context, nor does it mean that all stutterers must be treated in the same way. The reinforcement technique may be used to work on only one aspect at a time, although it may be an important one. At some point in treatment, nearly all therapists will want to work on the symptoms themselves. For this purpose, nonreinforcement is an excellent technique.

Behavior modification approaches may also serve an important function by making the clinician more thoroughly aware of his own role as a reinforcing agent, for better or for worse. It is, however, equally important that the therapist not become, or even consider himself, as a reinforcement machine. The therapist's role as a reinforcer is only a single aspect of his broader role as a therapist.

127

The "Establishment" of False Fluency

Since stutterers are already fluent much of the time, the operant claim to have "established" fluency is open to question. For noncommunicative, autistic, or retarded patients, "establishment" may really refer to the acquisition of a new response, but in stuttering the "establishment" of fluency hardly rates as much of an achievement.

Furthermore, since stuttering is motivated by fear and conflict, an increase in the level of fluency, by itself, is quite meaningless. It must be accompanied by changes in anxiety level and in one of the two opposing tendencies of the conflict. But since the operant approach denies itself the use of constructs, anxiety and conflict tend to be ignored. This leads to the serious fallacy that immediate fluency is good no matter how obtained. Immediate fluency provides only the illusion of improvement. Can it be maintained under all conditions, particularly under stress and anxiety? Unless fear and avoidance responses have been reduced along with struggle behaviors, the stutterer who encounters difficult conditions with no more preparation than a little practice speaking fluently will revert all the way back to ground zero.

The crucial question is one of stimulus conditions, both external and internal. Fluency "established" in the sheltered environment of the laboratory can disintegrate rapidly under the disorganizing impact of anxiety. The stutterer has to learn to stutter without the old anxiety, and he has to learn to be anxious without stuttering. But since anxiety is a construct, observable only by its effect, for some operant conditioners it does not exist. They would exile it from science. Presumably they would also exile such constructs as contained in the equation $e = mc^2$.

Where Are the Results?

No one seriously challenges the principle of reinforcement as an empirical fact. Both rewards and punishment can be observed to influence behavior. As Skinner notes,

> The commonest technique of control in modern life is punishment. The pattern is familiar: if a man does not behave as you wish, knock him down; if a child misbehaves, spank him; if the people of a country misbehave, bomb them. . . . All of this is done with the intention of reducing tendencies to behave in certain ways. Reinforcement builds up these tendencies; punishment is designed to tear them down. (Skinner, 1953)

Given the obviousness of the principle of reinforcement, the social impact of behavioral approaches, particular operant conditioning, is not surprising. But when we consider that operant techniques have now been applied to the autistic, the retarded, the schizophrenic, the phobic, and the delinquent, as well as the stutterer, we might expect that a considerable number of cures should have been produced if the technique is as effective as the articles reporting them artfully imply. There should be a number of ex-autistic, ex-retardates, post-psychotics, etc., at whom the proponents of operant conditioning in the clinic could point with pride. But where are they? Everyone seems to be saying that operant conditioning techniques have been revolutionizing therapy, but there is a scarce supply of successfully treated patients walking around to prove it. Operationally speaking, we challenge the evidence. Verbal claims, particularly when couched in the obscurity of jargon—"instatement," "schedules," "contingencies"—cannot serve as a substitute for hard evidence. On the other hand, with avoidance-reduction therapy, we can prove successful recoveries from at least the social and occupational handicap of stuttering. Some are prominent speech pathologists. A carefully designed study of the outcome of avoidance-reduction therapy, such as those of Van Riper, Sheehan, and Williams, has provided recent evidence supporting their efficacy (Gregory, 1969). Has speech pathology not already done better than operant conditioning?

The Language of Operant Conditioning

The self-consciously scientific language of operant conditioning is not without animism and circularity. Here are some examples:

(1) in operant language behaviors are supposed to "generate" the consequences that follow them. The statement appears too frequently to be dismissed as a figure of speech. But since behaviors don't really "generate" anything, the use of the term is inappropriate. Similarly, does a "schedule" in any scientific or operational sense "control" anything? Doesn't the experimenter really do the controlling, despite the operant claim that the subject determines his own reinforcement?

(2) The operant conditioners emphasize quantification and precision. These are highly commendable goals and have been for all psychology for a long time. But some operant conditioners write as if they had discovered these things, or at least as if they are the only clinicians who were precise in observing and quantifying behavior. They have themselves programmed to repeat these terms at annoyingly frequent intervals. True precision lies in careful methodology, not in the use of the terms describing it. Therapists may be easily overwhelmed, feeling that this is the only true science calling and that they must follow.

(3) Some operant conditioners claim that they are able to specify all the variables with precision. Even when not claimed, the reporting style often implies it. In psychology, however, it is axiomatic that all human observation contains ingredients of abstraction, of selecting out certain elements of a situation and excluding others. We never see *all* that might be going on. It is worth

129

noting that the operant conditioners in this publication are not guilty of this error, although a number of their colleagues are.

(4) One of the basic operant propositions is that behavior is determined by its consequences. Although true as an observation, this statement does not explain anything, but is instead a way of avoiding explanation. It is always possible to say, after the fact, that the consequences "controlled" the behavior, since by definition behavior is always determined by its consequences. The circularity is at least specifiable and precise.

(5) "Punishment" is often defined as anything which produces a decrease in the frequency of stuttering. This type of definition, however, often results in a tautology. If "punishment" can be inferred automatically from the observation of reductions in stuttering frequency, then the case for punishment as a means for reducing stuttering is established beyond dispute. If "punishment" equals improvement, then of course "punishment" works.

(6) Similarly, it is often suggested that many things done by therapists are punishing. This may be true in the special terminology indicated above in paragraph 5. But the therapist looking for guidance may be led to believe that punishment, in the English rather than the operant language, is meant. He or she may then feel sanctioned to try "punishment"—the direct kind, not the inferred kind. And stutterers have experienced real punishment all their lives—they don't need a therapist invited to try more.

(7) It has long been observed that theories differ more than therapies do. Behavior therapists generally and operant conditioners specifically illustrate this tendency well. From their therapy descriptions, it is clear that the operant conditioners are working in a clinical context. They require the same "intuitive" processes as others. Shames' broadly clinical language illustrates this point. And Ryan's programming seems aimed at systematizing the clinical practice of stuttering therapy. Each, however, seem to include goals from the old avoidance-of-stuttering school discussed earlier. In our view, to work for successful avoidance and for avoidance-reduction at the same time is to work at cross-purposes.

The Problem of Outcome Evaluation

One of the tricky features of doing therapy with stuttering is that almost anything designed to bring about immediate fluency may work, at least temporarily. The experimenter who uses an operant approach and defines reinforcement by observing an increase in the frequency of a response, may easily be misled. What he sees as reinforcement may be no more than a reduction of stuttering frequency caused by the novelty and artificiality of the stimulus.

One of the most notable things about operant conditioning is the startling claims made by some about the percentages of recovery or improvement. One operant conditioner told the International Seminar on Behavior Therapy for Stuttering that he had cured 40 out of 40 stutterers by his program. According to his report, they all spoke fluently, and the fluency lasted for all. However, out of eight stutterers that we know of who have gone through his program, seven reported no improvement. The eighth stutterer reports his improvement in a vocal cadence that sounds like Tik-Tok of Oz.

In writing, these claims tend to be less sweeping, although a high rate of improvement is commonly claimed as an outcome of operant procedures. To our knowledge, there has been no independent verification and follow-up of these reported cures by operant conditioning, either in stuttering or with other disturbances.

Research designed to evaluate the outcome of therapy is extraordinarily difficult to do for a number of different reasons, so it is not too surprising that there is little hard evidence that one type of therapy is any better than any other. One of the difficulties in evaluating the effect of a therapeutic technique is the fact that even the experimenter or clinician may exert important psychotherapeutic effects. And, what the behavior therapists actually do is more in line with traditional psychotherapy than their formal statements might lead us to believe. In the process, many stray rather far from the traditions of experimental psychology. They reveal, in their case reports, a clinical sensitivity and psychotherapeutic orientation that may have as much to do with the outcome of therapy as any of their formally described schedules. Although this may be a tribute to their individual clinical skills, it signifies that pure behavior therapy is largely a myth.

Punishment

One of the most active operant conditioners of stuttering, Siegel (1969), has reopened the case for the use of punishment:

... For the past several years, Dick Martin and I have been involved in a program of research dealing with the modification of disfluencies in stutterers and normal speakers.

In these experiments, we have primarily used a punishment paradigm. Our interest in punishment stems from several sources. For one, the notion that stuttering develops when some aspect of the child's early speech behavior is punished is a very pervasive one. Second, the presumed role of social punishment in maintaining stuttering has always been confusing. There seems to be a rather widely held view that any event that increases the penalty for stuttering will also increase the frequency of these behaviors. This reaches so far into our folklore of stuttering therapy, that we are even admonished that it is dangerous to reward fluency, since, by implication, we

131

thereby suggest to the stutterer that we disapprove of his disfluencies.

There have been virtually no experiments to support these contentions about the relationship between stuttering and punishment. Many years ago, Van Riper (1937) reported that the threat of shock resulted in increased moments of stuttering. These findings have never been replicated in any published report to my knowledge, though Frick (1951) included a comparable condition in his Ph.D. thesis. (Siegel, 1969)

It is not accurate to say that there is a folklore of stuttering therapy which admonishes that it is dangerous to *reward* fluency. Of course, it is dangerous to *compliment* a child or an adult for fluency, for if fluency is so good then stuttering must be bad. The step in logic is simple.

Any plea for the use of punishment as a therapeutic technique must be viewed as a step backward. First of all there is ample evidence that penalty increases the frequency of stuttering, at least for the majority of stutterers. Also, if punishment were effective in eliminating stuttering, stuttering would not exist. But instead of eliminating stuttering, punishment leads to escape behaviors and ultimately to self-reinforcing avoidance. Furthermore, the punished child who is engaged in avoidance will never give himself the chance to find out if circumstances have changed so that the punishment is no longer there. It is also important that you cannot punish stuttering without punishing the act of speaking in the process.

The relationship of punishment to stuttering is curious, paradoxical, and probably very important. Some experimenters use the term *penalty* for generally negative consequences and reserve the term *punishment* for response-contingent penalty. Obviously, stuttering is punished more than it is rewarded, at least in the broader sense of the word *punishment*. Insofar as stuttering is also punished more than it is rewarded in the narrow sense, it appears to go counter to the Law of Effect. There have been a number of theoretical suggestions to explain this paradox. In any event it is probable that both punishment and intermittent positive reinforcement make stuttering a response cluster unusually resistant to extinction.

Life is too full of punishment to make it necessary or advisable to administer more of it in the clinic. Therapists who use punishment are probably incompetent to use anything else, or they have a neurotic need to assume the role of the punisher as a reassurance against their own fear of being in the role of the one punished. We have never encountered stutterers whose case histories lacked an abundance of punishment. They have been punished too much, not too little. And, if punishment were in any way effective, every stutterer would have been cured in childhood. Can the experimenter hope to outpunish the parents who produced the problem in the first place?

After all, what are fear and anxiety but the anticipation of future punishment, resulting from a punishment experienced in the past? Skinner, the father of operant conditioning, has eloquently warned of the ineffectiveness of punishment as a method of behavior change.

The effect of punishment was a temporary suppression of the behavior, not a reduction in the total number of responses. Even under severe and prolonged punishment, the rate of responding will rise when punishment has been discontinued, and although under these circumstances it is not easy to show that all the responses originally available will appear, it has been found that after a given time the rate of responding is no lower than if no punishment had taken place. (Skinner, 1953)

Elsewhere, Skinner has pointed out not only the limitations but the unfortuante by-products of punishment.

The evidence for the effectiveness of punishment is at best conflicting. In an expanded replication of a study by Flanagan, Goldiamond, and Azrin, six male stutterers enrolled in the psychology speech clinic of the University of California, Los Angeles, were tested during successive readings of a given passage. There were three experimental conditions in which a 4,000 cps tone at an intensity of 108 dB, ISO hearing level, was used: (1) an aversive condition in which the presentation of the tone was contingent upon stuttering, (2) an escape condition in which the cessation of the tone was contingent upon stuttering, and (3) a random condition in which the tone was presented independent of the subjects' disfluencies.

The findings, contrary to those of Flanagan, Goldiamond, and Azrin, were that stuttering decreased in all conditions. The results were most readily explained as being due to the distraction effect. Since random noise also reduced stuttering, nothing of a "contingent" nature went on. The subjects in our experiment rated the noise as not really punishing but somewhat distracting. If punishing at all, the supposedly noxious sound involved a fairly mild penalty. The experience of stuttering itself, which the allegedly "aversive" stimulus was supposed to control, was rated as still more punishing than the noise (Biggs and Sheehan, 1969). Since the original operant study flunked the scientific test of repeatability, we are skeptical of claims made for operant methods and are reluctant to recommend such techniques to the practicing clinician.

The Relationship of Behavior Therapy and Psychotherapy

Behavior therapy seems to involve symptomatic therapy at its most symptomatic. With previous stuttering therapies, it was at least possible to place the techniques in a context that considered the case history and the reactions of the individual. The person was treated, not just the problem. In this respect, behavior modification is a definite step backward.

The child who stutters is still in the throes of the pressures that produced the problem in the first place. Do the operant conditioners take into account the present and the future actions of the parents? The parents are going to be just as influential in shaping behavior as the "program," no matter how ingeniously that program is conceived.

The adult stutterer too is not immune to the defensive and secondary gain aspects of stuttering. Some stutterers sabotage themselves and the therapist at every turn. We find it curious that a "new" therapy suddenly assumes that such possibilities do not exist. We suspect that when real evaluation and follow-up are performed on the behavior therapies, the phenomena of resistance and relapse will be given diplomatic recognition.

We feel that thus far the influence of behavior therapy on stuttering treatment has been mostly retrogressive. Discarded and discredited devices of the past have been exhumed with little that is new except for language and instrumentation. Wingate even makes a direct plea for the resurrection:

> This explanation suggests new avenues of approach to basic research in stuttering as well as pointing up the value of reviving areas of exploration initiated, but abandoned, a number of years ago. (Wingate, 1969)

Our hope for discovery lies in the future, in methods that have not yet been tried and found wanting, not in combing over the rubbish of centuries.

The Psychotherapeutic Context of Behavior Modification

All therapy is an interpersonal event, and its outcome hinges on a number of interactions between the therapist and his clinician. Consequently, whatever technique is to be used must be appropriate for the client. There is nothing about the behavior modification techniques which excludes them from this general principle. In fact, it may be argued that since behavioral techniques focus on external events, on the outwardly observable, the clinician who uses them should be more, not less, aware of the general context of therapy, of the individual, and of his progress in the therapeutic sequence. Unfortunately, however, the literature on behavior modification is usually devoid of this awareness, and in the case of the operant conditioners particularly, attending to observables only is a point of professional pride.

Many stutterers, as a part of their tendency toward avoidance, shed the responsibility for their behavior. They have to realize that stuttering is something they have learned and something they can unlearn. A device, such as a portable masking noise generator, or a delayed auditory feedback device, has all the magical properties that any wishful stutterer could hope for. A machine that will cure you of stuttering! It is better than the pink pill. A series of conditioning trials that will rid you of the nasty habit. And you don't have to get personally involved; neither does your therapist. What more could you hope for? Perhaps it is worth noting that quacks have begun to spring up armed with these devices, since they lend themselves so readily to quackery. In the *Los Angeles Times*, ads have begun to appear inviting seekers of the holy grail of quick fluency to step up and pay the price. The machine has now been found, and you may buy it. Although unquestionably most operant conditioners are sincere clinicians working for the benefit of their clients, the ready adaptation of hardware to quackery by the irresponsible is a limitation not to be taken lightly.

How can behavior modification be made to fit into the general context of psychotherapy? The behavior modification movement has paved its way more with enthusiastic claim and sweeping promise than with self-skepticism and scientific caution. Furthermore, almost nothing has been done to place these behavior modification techniques within the framework of broadly defined psychotherapy. And stuttering therapy is no more than an array of specialized techniques for a special form of psychotherapy. Even if the claims of behavior modification techniques are sustained—and this has yet to be proved—how can we integrate their methods into a psychotherapeutic context? This remains one of the great unanswered questions.

References

Bandura, A., *Principles of Behavior Modification*. New York: Holt, 1969.

Biggs, B. E., and J. G. Sheehan, "Punishment or Distraction? Operant Stuttering Revisited," *Journal of Abnormal Psychology*, LXXIV, (1969) 256-62.

Breger, L., and J. L. McGaugh, "Critique and Reformulation of 'Learning Theory' Approaches to Psychotherapy and Neurosis," *Psychological Bulletin*, LXIII (1965), 338-58.

Dunlap, K., *Habits: Their Making and Unmaking*. New York: Liveright, 1932.

Gregory, H. H., *An Assessment of the Results of Stuttering Therapy*. Final report, Research and Demonstration Project 1725-S, Social and Rehabilitation Service, U. S. Department of Health, Education, and Welfare, 1969.

Hilgard, E. R., and D. G. Marquis, *Conditioning and Learning*. New York: Appleton-Century, 1940.

Sheehan, J. G., "Modification of Stuttering Through Non-reinforcement," *Journal of Abnormal and Social Psychology*, XLVI (1951), 51-63.

——. "Theory and Treatment of Stuttering as an Approach-Avoidance Conflict," *Journal of Psychology*, XXXVI (1953), 27-49.

——. "An Integration of Psychotherapy and Speech Therapy Through a Conflict Theory of Stuttering," *Journal of Speech and Hearing Disorders*, XIX (1954), 474-82.

——*Stuttering: Research and Therapy*. New York: Harper, 1970.

Sheehan, J. G., and R. B. Voas, "Stuttering as Conflict: A Comparison of Therapy Techniques Involving Approach and Avoidance," *Journal of Speech and Hearing Disorders*, XXII (1957), 714-23.

Siegel, G., "Experimental Modification of Speech Dysfluency." In B. Gray and G. England (eds.), *Stuttering and the Conditioning Therapies*. Monterey, Calif.: Monterey Institute for Speech and Hearing, 1969.

Skinner, B. F., *Science and Human Behavior*. New York: Macmillan, 1953.

Van Riper, C., "The Effect of Penalty upon the Frequency of Stuttering Spasms," *Journal of Genetic Psychology*, L. (1937), 193-95.

––. *Speech Correction: Principles and Methods, 4th Ed.* Englewood Cliffs, N. J.: Prentice-Hall, 1963.

Wingate, M. E., "Sound and Pattern in 'Artificial' Fluency," *Journal of Speech and Hearing Research*, XII (1969), 677-86.

PART IV

Report and Commentary

Report and Commentary

STANLEY AINSWORTH, Ph. D.

We wish that all of you could have attended the Conference as silent and invisible observers. If you could have heard the nuance of a phrase, judged the personality of its speaker, or tasted the flavor of discussion, you would have gained a much deeper understanding of the material. We hope the following comments give you some idea of these subtleties. We also want to tell you of the way we influenced each other, and of a few ideas we decided to add or emphasize.

General Comments

We talked a lot. We often disagreed. Although sometimes, as we expressed ourselves more completely and accurately, the disagreements tended to fade, and ideas from two or more sources merged into a more unified formulation. At other times, we settled back into our own unique and individual points of view without being convinced—but always with the nagging doubt that perhaps we had not listened well enough. One idea with which you are all familiar was illustrated many times. Any single approach to the understanding or treatment of stuttering does not satisfy all we know (or think we do) about this puzzling problem. We were frustrated often because we could not explain or account for these inadequacies satisfactorally. It was not possible even for this august group. So we often had to stop, after considerable verbal struggling, aware that there is still much confusion, weakness, divergence, and challenge. If you had been there, you would have been able to identify these occasions because it was at these times that people began to repeat themselves and raise their voices and everyone began to talk at once.

We began planning for this book early in 1969. After we had determined who would write what, the first drafts of each chapter were prepared, and these were reacted to in writing by all of the participants. The second drafts were then prepared for discussion and final editing at the Conference in Jamaica. We did not try, as in previous conferences, to reach agreement by all to the content of the individually prepared material, but each author was called on repeatedly to defend not only his ideas but also the manner in which they were written. As a further refinement, we had the continuous participation of a professional editor who is also a speech pathologist. We even considered putting in some "rebuttal" or a detailed discussion of the controversial points, but we thought the book was probably too long already to have the impact we hoped

139

for. We are aware that the book is neither complete nor symmetrical. We have not tried to present all forms of behavior modification. It has already been noted that although Dr. Ryan's chapter provides an example of Dr. Shames' operant conditioning, Dr. Damsté's chapter does not illustrate Dr. Brutten's two-factor theory. Dr. Sheehan's chapter is largely a reaction to operant conditioning rather than to behavior modification as a whole. It just wasn't possible to present more than an abbreviated and incomplete picture in one small book.

Those of you who are familiar with the previous writings of some of the authors may have noted that the ideas in this book represent a movement from earlier writings. You may also feel that some of the authors are attending to behaviors not usually included as stuttering by others in the same area of activity. These differences should not puzzle you. They illustrate the evolving and dynamic nature of attempts to develop more effective therapy for stuttering. As theories are applied to therapy for stutterers, some problems arise that can be solved best by changing the theory. Others are best resolved by extending the use of current procedures without violating the principles on which they are based.

Some Repeated Concerns

We were primarily concerned with *your* reaction. Would you see the book as a "sell" job for behavior modification? Would you find in it so many conflicting ideas that you understood the whole process no better than before? Would you feel that behavior modification was no different from what you had been doing all along and that the only new thing was the jargon? Would you oversimplify and see only a choice between a broad and flexible therapy and one that is narrow and rigid? We hoped that you would avoid any of these extreme reactions. True enough, in much of the book we emphasized external rather than internal responses, but we were trying to give you specific and clear illustrations of the concepts. We felt that if you came to understand the principles you would be able to use them in analyzing the more subtle behaviors.

We were all concerned about how you and some of our colleagues in related fields would react to statements that presented only part of the picture. We knew that we had been incomplete. We knew that some of our statements did not reflect all of the variations, all of the points of view, or all the degrees of emphasis of those who are called "behaviorists" or "operant people." The categories and classifications we devised were used in order to clarify and simplify; they do not represent all that we may have wanted to say.

We did not want to recommend that you use behavior modification techniques, and one of our concerns was whether the book contained enough cautions against its use by inadequately trained people. It seems clear that behavior modification, like other therapies, can do harm to the stutterer if it is misused or if it is used with inadequate understanding. In this way, and in other ways, behavior modification is similar to other procedures for changing the behavior of clients. There are some, not in the Conference group, who are concerned that behavior modification procedures are too manipulative, that clients will be pushed along a path determined by the clinician regardless of his own desires. We felt, generally, that this likelihood was no greater for behavior modification techniques than for many other forms of therapy. One possible type of misuse comes from an implied justification in the writings of operant conditioners for the extensive use of "punishment." This misunderstanding may arise from the use of the concept in the colloquial sense rather than in its more restrictive and specific meaning of "punishment" in operant conditioning. We tried to show that the clinician may profit from looking to conditioning which facilitates or inhibits responding rather than trying to determine if the procedure is "punishing" or not, provided he realizes that under different circumstances and at different times what suppresses or facilitates behavior will change. It should also be pointed out that the two-factor theory takes a strong stand against punishment, in *both* the colloquial and the restrictive sense. Another way in which behavior modification techniques might be misused is in the misinterpretation of increased fluency. Most of us felt that the clinician should retain his suspicion of quick and easy flights into fluency by the stutterer. The operant conditioners, however, would hasten to add that with appropriate programming, fluency, however obtained, can be brought under stimulus control and moved out into the environment, although they realize that this transfer is a problematic aspect of therapy. Both operant conditioning and two-factor techniques are amenable to misuse by "quacks," but responsible therapists are concerned about long-range as well as short-term gains.

A Sampling of the Ideas Discussed

It is hard to describe adequately the range of topics, the flow of interrelated concepts, and the depth of discussion. It may help to visualize the wealth of detail in the first three parts of the book and then realize that nearly every page stirred some response from one or more of the participants. Comments, questions, arguments, and challenges ranged from the abstrusely theoretical to the emminently practical. Editorial suggestions mingled with difficult concepts about the meaning and implications of a therapeutic procedure. Sometimes we zeroed in on minute details; at other times we concentrated on broad philosophical considerations. Many times, a stimulating line of discussion could not be followed through to a satisfying conclusion because of the practical pressure of preparing this book for publication. The pattern of discussion was free-flowing, almost amorphous, but certain ideas appeared with notable frequency and

141

intensity. A description of a few of these ideas may add to your understanding of this book, and they may stimulate your thinking as they did ours.

We had some differences over definitions. Should we use "behavior therapy" or "behavior modification"? The terms are similar in meaning but different in history and connotation. They are also used by different people—you can tell something about the way a person was trained by which term he uses. Furthermore, other terms (punishment/reward, extinction, classical/respondent, operant/instrumental) present similar problems. We did not want all the permutations of meanings to get in the way of your apprehension of the content of these chapters. So we composed a glossary in which you can pursue these definitional differences without losing your train of thought. We decided to use the terms that were most comfortable for the participants—a distinctly practical approach.

Sometimes, our differences went deeper than our different definitions of key terms. We all organize the events that take place in our universe into what seems to be the best way from our own personal point of view. When two people reach this level in communication, their disagreements arise from difficulties in basic understanding—until they know the point of view from which the other person is operating. Stuttering, in its infinite variety, seems to encourage this particular kind of disagreement. Also, the way we organize and classify events concerned with stuttering varies with the purpose for which we are doing the organizing. Whatever our system may be, there is always a "residue" that we cannot fit into the framework. As a result, we exclude from our organization of "stuttering" whatever does not fit the framework. Behavior modification theories of stuttering do the same thing; they limit stuttering to certain behaviors or phenomena and consider other phenomena as something other than stuttering. But we should not be too critical of this. It results more from the limitations of human thinking than from the limitations of behavior modification. Probably all theories of stuttering and approaches to therapy have built-in, systematic limitations. Any therapist selects examples of behavior as representative of stuttering. The selection would probably not be acceptable to clinicians of different points of view. Even those of us who use an eclectic or pragmatic approach to therapy are limited by what we can control or manage. We are all left with the necessity of making our own individual judgments as to what we will choose to include in our framework of theory and therapy for stuttering.

Some of our theoretical discussions may interest you. They tended to drift into long interchanges, for professors love dearly to manipulate the infinite permutations possible in the theoretical consideration of a problem. However, the focus of this conference was on therapy, and this kept theory from going too far astray. In fact, the practicality of a theory was put to the test many times as we took a hard look at the therapeutic procedures it generated.

As might be expected, many of our theoretical discussions centered around the meanings of words, many of which overlapped and varied. "Punishment" and "reward" have already been mentioned as difficult concepts. "Counterconditioning," "deconditioning," and "desensitization" were also discussed at some length because the differences in their meaning determine in large measure the strategy of their use in therapy. We argued about the term "extinguish" because it implies that "extinguished" responses have disappeared, when in fact they may only have been reduced.

We argued about the difficulty of identifying the unconditioned stimulus in stuttering. This topic is important, particularly for the two-factor theory, in determining therapeutic procedures. Extinction in classical conditioning is the presentation of the conditioned stimulus in the absence of the unconditioned stimulus, consequently, one must know what the unconditioned stimulus is in order to be certain it is absent while trying to achieve extinction. The answer to this objection against the two-factor theory is that whatever the unconditioned stimulus is we know by its function that it must be noxious, and consequently we remove all noxious stimulation from the therapy situation. By so doing, we should be able to achieve extinction of the conditioned response.

We also argued about the level of awareness (or unawareness) at which the conditioning of instrumental (operant) responses took place. If a response is learned for the purpose of escaping or avoiding nonfluency, one would expect the stutterer to be aware of it. Yet many of the behaviors of stutterers apparently occur below the awareness level. One of the suggestions for resolving this paradox was that the responses start out as voluntary, purposive behaviors that are performed with full awareness, but that with constant performance they become automatic, habitual, and almost involuntary, until their occurrence drops well below the level of awareness.

There was substantial discussion about what makes a response "maladaptive." Most of us felt that whether a behavior was identified as adaptive or maladaptive should depend on the effect the behavior has on the stutterer and on those around him. Such approach recognizes the relative and changing nature of the situation. Behaviors might be judged differently at different times and in different situations by different people. Furthermore, a behavior recognized as maladaptive may continue because its cost to the client is "worth it" for the results it obtains, or because it is felt to be less "punishing" than an alternative.

With both operant and two-factor proponents present, it was not surprising that we argued at great length about whether repetitions and prolongations resulted from instrumental conditioning, from classical conditioning, or whether they were a physiological breakdown precipitated by conditioned emotion. The long disagreement resolved in the end on a philosophical difference. From the operant point of view, any physiological or organismic event is a response. Even an event that takes place at the cellular level, such as progressive baldness (which was somewhat snidely used as an example), is a response, although it is a cellular response. In other words, the concept of "response" is simply a way of dividing up ongoing organismic events so that they can be mentally and linguistically manipulated. For the two-factor position, however, there are a number of organismic events which are not responses. The disorganization of fluent speech that occurs when sounds and syllables are repeated or prolonged is one of these nonresponses. It is instead an event analogous to response-suppression. "Response-suppression" is simply a decrease in the amount of responding which occurs when an organism is experiencing anxiety. The decrease in responding is an event, but it is not, from the two-factor point of view, a response. Similarly, the disorganization of responding that takes place during the production of repetitions and prolongations is an event, but it is not a response.

Whenever we discussed the operant approach we found ourselves talking about measurement. All of the operant approaches involve counting. But, the other members of the Conference kept asking, what is to be counted? Decisions must be made about what to observe and what not to observe, and these decisions will reflect the clinician's consideration of what aspects of stuttering behavior are important and what are not. The question thus resolves, again, on a theoretical or philosophical question. The discussion on measurement also frequently centered around whether or not there were aspects of stuttering that are not measurable, such as "silence" or "anticipation." Counting stuttered words may be reliable, but this reliability may not be as important as the *validity,* or the relevance of what is counted. Furthermore, the counting of disfluencies assumes that they represent equal intervals on a scale of fluency, but surely some disfluencies are more disfluent than others, even within the same subject. Also related to the question of measurement is the use of a "base rate," and the establishment of such a base rate by counting. Obviously where you "go" in therapy depends on where you start. The term "base rate" may not be descriptive of anything because of the variability of the behavior being counted.

Although we had some questions, and some comments, about the use of counting in the use of operant procedures, we do not want to disregard their value. They should serve to alert you to some of the vulnerabilities of any therapeutic process. Whatever technique you use, you must have *measures* of behavior rather than general judgment. Counting is *one* of the measures you can use. You may want to expand the measurement process to other aspects of stuttering that are less easily observed, find ways to demonstrate

144

their existence, and then apply counting or some other systematic, specific, and carefully prepared method of measurement. It is the process that matters, not the material being processed. One answer to the objection that counting stuttered words is a limiting procedure is that the other aspects of stuttering may drop out as therapy progresses. In your therapy, you will always have to make judgments about "validity"—you will have to decide what needs changing the most and what technique will bring about the desired change most effectively. We hope that these comments and questions will help you become more aware of this process so that you will try to be more systematic and more precise in the way you measure therapeutic progress.

One thing we all agreed on after our discussion of measurement: there is a great need for more clinical data for the success or lack of success obtained with the use of various procedures. Clinicians of all persuasions must build into their therapy the procedures for collecting and reporting the data by which the success of their procedures can be evaluated. If it does nothing else, this book will have been successful if it helps you learn some improved ways to measure degrees of clinical success.

There is one critical factor in any therapy about which we were not able to provide much guidance in this book: the selection of what is done next in the therapeutic process at any of several decision points. The literature of operant conditioning has given some attention to this process. Indeed, the formulation of a program, at least if done well, will anticipate these different decision points and make the decisions in advance, taking into account all of the different possible contributing factors. One might question whether it is possible to anticipate all of these factors accurately, and, if not, an extreme reliance on the program might cause an unanticipated factor to be overlooked. The two-factor therapy starts at the bottom of the hierarchy with situations that are less emotional and works up to the most severely threatening situations. This is a general strategy for therapy, and it is made specific to the individual by constructing the hierarchy for the specific situations that the stutterer provides. Again, however, this procedure is open to criticism for making the decision in advance, which may cause trouble when unanticipated events take place. These are only general directions, but quite frankly, we did not see how we could provide any more specific or definitive directions for making such judgments. Although we did not provide much direction, your experience and clinical sensitivity to the needs of another human being will not fail you.

We also considered the importance of the therapist himself in the effectiveness of therapy. Dr. Damsté stressed the importance of a warm, reassuring, accepting environment for the success of his therapeutic techniques. We all wondered to what degree confidence in the clinician or in the process play a part in improvement with any technique. Does the kind of person the therapist is influence the results? Is some of the effect due simply to the massive quantity of attention centered on the client for a period of time? Does it make any difference if therapy is distributed or relatively continuous—or is effective therapy a result of crucial moments that cannot be predicted? Clearly the objective descriptions presented in this book do not portray what came out in the Conference discussions regarding these points. We all discovered that no matter how mechanically or objectively we described procedures, the therapist in all of us comes out when we work with stutterers, and we provide more than just the cold bones of the process. Other than this, however, we found it necessary to leave these questions unanswered, but we all felt that no matter how mechanical or objective the process of therapy may be, all clinicians must be aware of the potential of these "psychological" influences if they are to retain an appropriate clinical perspective. Obviously, classical and operant conditioning do not explain all things about stuttering. What a therapist may do with a stutterer, at least in our present state of ignorance and uncertainty, goes beyond what can be identified as behavior modification.

Conclusion

As you can see, the Conference, and the book, are like so many other events in our lives—incomplete, inconsistant, frag-mentary—sources more of stimulating questions than of satisfying answers. We did have some unique circumstances. The room where the discussions were held had a wide double door open to the beach and the ocean. When the situation became too involved, we released tension with a walk beside the blue-green sea. The room was also near the end of the runway of a busy airport. Throughout the day, jets roared overhead, just clearing the treetops. Arguments, speeches, rare gems of philosophy, all were cut off in midstream as we held an enforced period of "silence," plugged our ears, and waited. Perhaps this contributed to the fragmentary nature of what we tried to accomplish. In any event, you should read these words with the thunder of jet planes in your ears to participate wholly in the atmosphere of their inception.

Perhaps one bit of caution should be stressed. This book does not thoroughly cover the ground of behavior modification techniques. It is a beginning, and we hope it will be helpful to you in learning more from the readings suggested and from other sources. We are confident that conscientious clinicians will not try to use these or any other procedures until they have obtained adequate information and, usually, appropriately monitored experience in the use of them.

Regardless of how you use the ideas expressed in this book, we hope that it will help you understand your own therapy more completely. This improved understanding will come about if you become more sensitive to the effect that your behavior will have on the stutterer, whether or not you attempt to use behavior modification in any systematic way. If this alone can be translated into your day-to-day interactions with stutterers, our efforts will have been worthwhile.

GLOSSARY

C. WOODRUFF STARKWEATHER, Ph.D.

In the world of science, there is a great effort to achieve precision of language, and perhaps the unquestioned success that science has achieved is partly a result of its crystalline terminology. But the achievement of precise terms has its drawbacks.

One drawback is that we come to expect new, and carefully used words when we read scientific material. Usually, the newest words are used the most often. So, when we find a word, even a very familiar one, occurring over and over again in a scientific publication, we suspect the author is using it in a specialized sense. When other authors do the same thing, we are convinced that a new, scientifically precise, carefully defined, and eminently useful word has entered the language. Such a word acquires a very bright halo. The most respected authors use it all the time. Overuse, however, does not always mean that a word has a new meaning. Perhaps the old meaning acquired a new relevance. In such cases, the reader often assumes that the word means something other than it used to, much as we might not recognize an old friend, if we saw him hobnobbing with royalty. In behaviorism, words such as *frequency, consequences,* and *contingent* have taken on this kind of an aura. But be careful. Some common words have acquired new meanings, such as *observable* and *reinforcement.* Both types of words are identified in this glossary.

Another drawback to the use of precise definitions in science occurs when two schools of scientific thought arise concerning the same subject. People being what they are, those who hold such different opinions don't care too much to communicate with each other, so they invent different terms for the same concepts. Long after the original controversy has died down, younger scientists trained in the two schools find that they can't talk to each other. Even when they know they are talking about the same events, the different terms have acquired a connotation that is hard to shake loose. This is why there are both operant and two-factor terms and why two *speech pathologists,* trained in different schools of behaviorism but both concerned with stuttering, may have difficulty communicating with each other. In the glossary that follows, words that are used exclusively by one school or the other are so indicated.

149

acquisition A progressive increment in the frequency at which a response occurs as the result of a conditioning procedure. In instrumental conditioning, reinforcement, positive or negative, is the procedure for achieving acquisition. In classical conditioning, one stimulus is made contingent on another in order to achieve acquisition.

adaptive response An instrumentally conditioned response that enables an organism to avoid or escape objective danger, or to approach or achieve reinforcement in a relatively efficient manner. A two-factor term.

adjustive response A term encompassing both adaptive and maladaptive responses. Specifically, an instrumentally conditioned response the reinforcement for which is achieved when the organism makes an adjustment in the stimulus situation or in his relationship to it (by leaving it, for example) so that there is either a decrease in negative stimulation or an increase in positive stimulation. A two-factor term.

behavior The ongoing, continuous activity of an organism. A number of responses. One response. Usually *behavior* refers to continuous responding, while *responses* are units of behavior, much like minutes are units of time.

behavior modification A general term for any of a variety of clinical procedures, based on learning theory and conditioning principles, for changing the behavior of clients, either by removing or reducing undesirable behaviors or producing desirable ones.

branching steps In a program, a series of optional conditioning activities which are decided upon on the basis of the client's behavior during an earlier part of the program. An operant term.

classical conditioning Called respondent conditioning by operant conditioners. Any of a variety of procedures in which the experimenter or clinician arranges for a stimulus, which he is confident will produce a specific response, to occur consistently after another stimulus, which he is equally confident will *not* produce the same response. After a number of such presentations, the response, or a version of it, will occur after the first stimulus as well as after the second. This process is often theorized to be the way in which involuntary, smooth muscle, autonomic nervous system responses are learned. For example, we become frightened (our palms sweat and our hearts beat faster) at the sight of the dentist because in the past his appearance has always been followed by pain. We salivate at the sound of pots and pans rattling in the kitchen because in the past those sounds were consistently followed by eating.

concomitant behavior A response, or a number of responses, occurring at approximately the same time as a response that is being contingently stimulated. The concomitant behaviors are not stimu-

150

lated contingently, although the stimulation will occasionally follow their occurrence by accident. A two-factor term.

conditioned inhibition A relatively permanent, learned reduction in the strength of a response caused by the repeated association of temporary reductions in response strength (see reactive inhibition) with certain stimuli. Through classical conditioning, the stimuli become capable of eliciting a decrease in responding. A two-factor theoretical concept.

conditioned reinforcement Reinforcement the effectiveness of which depends on conditioning. Money is a good example. Someone who has never had any experience with money would not be aware of its value and would consequently not respond or work in order to obtain it.

conditioned response In classical conditioning, the response made, after a number of trials have taken place, upon presentation of the conditioned stimulus. The conditioned response usually resembles, and may even be identical to, the unconditioned response.

conditioned stimulus In classical conditioning, the stimulus that, after a number of trials, comes to result in the conditioned response. The conditioned stimulus is often a neutral stimulus that does not produce any particular response before conditioning. After conditioning, however, the conditioned stimulus becomes positive if the unconditioned stimulus was positive or negative if the unconditioned stimulus was negative.

conditioning Any of several procedures (see operant and classical conditioning) in which one arranges for certain stimuli to occur at certain times so that a particular response is made to occur either more often (acquisition) or less often (extinction). When a response that formerly occurred only rarely or not at all is conditioned to occur more often, learning is often assumed to have taken place, provided that the change is long-lasting. It is often theorized that all learning is a result of conditioning processes that take place either by chance or through the conscious manipulation of stimuli by others. Operant conditioners do not make either of these assumptions about learning but restrict their discussion, for the most part, to conditioning.

conditioning history The sum total of an organism's pertinent past experience with contingent stimulation. In order to describe an organism's conditioning history explicitly, one would need to describe in detail all the contingent stimuli to which it had been exposed, their schedules of administration, and so on. Since this is impossible, except in a controlled laboratory arrangement in animal research, the term is usually used much more loosely. In the clinic, one might speculate, for example, that a stutterer's conditioning history had included reinforcement for struggle behavior.

consequences This term is used so often (for good reasons) that it has acquired an aura and may be felt to mean more than its generic sense. It doesn't.

contingent Follows as a consequence of. A stimulus is contingent on a response if the occurrence of the response causes the occurrence of the stimulus. This relationship of causation may be prearranged by an experimenter or clinician. Thus, if a clinician decides to say "good" after five minutes of fluent speech, he has arranged for five minutes of fluent speech to result in the word "good." The word *contingent* has been used so much that it appears to have a specialized technical meaning, but this is not so.

control Usually referring to "stimulus control." A response is under stimulus control when the experimenter or clinician can reliably predict that when he presents the stimulus, the client or subject will produce the response. A response is brought under stimulus control by repeatedly reinforcing (or punishing) it in the presence of the stimulus. An operant word.

criterion A predetermined frequency of occurrence of a particular response, signifying the end of a portion of a program. A predetermined response or series of responses for which reinforcement is given. An operant word.

differential reinforcement Any procedure in which one response is reinforced and another, usually similar to the first one, is not. The procedure causes the reinforced response to occur more often and the nonreinforced response to occur less often simultaneously. It is a powerful technique for changing the *form* of a response by reinforcing only those responses that have the desired form or a similar one. See also shaping, which is a special use of differential reinforcement. An operant word.

discriminative stimulus In operant conditioning, a stimulus in the presence of which some particular consequence, such as punishment or reinforcement, will occur. The discriminative stimulus informs the subject, before he responds, what will happen after he responds.

extinction A progressive decrement in the frequency at which a response occurs, sometimes to the point where it fails to occur again. Procedures for achieving extinction may be identified as those in which the conditioned stimulus is presented in the absence of the unconditioned stimulus (for classical conditioning) or those in which the reinforcement is withdrawn (for operant conditioning).

fluency failure A term encompassing both stuttering and any other form of nonfluency, normal or otherwise. A two-factor word.

frequency One of the words that has been used so often that it has acquired an aura of technical jargon and may be suspected of meaning more than it does. It simply means how often something happens.

hierarchy   A list of stimulus situations, arranged by a client in an order representing the degree of negative emotion with which he reacts to them for use in determining the order in which desensitization will take place. A two-factor word.

informing stimulus   A stimulus, contingent on a response, the primary purpose of which is to inform the client that the response has just occurred. It may be a neutral, positive, or negative stimulus. A two-factor term.

instrumental conditioning   See "operant conditioning."

learning theory   Any of a variety of theories, based on the data from experiments involving instrumental and classical conditioning, that attempt to explain how learning takes place. The procedures of conditioning, which have been demonstrated to change the frequency of responding, are used differently by different learning theorists to explain how learning occurs. Most operant conditioners do not speculate extensively about how learning occurs and consequently do not use the term very often.

life situation procedures   Any clinical procedure in which an attempt is made to use conditioning techniques in the patient's day-to-day environment, usually his home, office, or school. Parents, teachers, friends, and colleagues are usually involved in administering various forms of stimulation according to a predetermined arrangement.

maintenance   (of a response)   The administration of occasional reinforcement to keep an already acquired response at some frequency of occurrence. More reinforcement would result in a further increase in frequency (assuming the response is not at some maximum frequency) and less reinforcement would produce extinction. The term is of particular importance in discussions of stuttering, for which one must explain how the behavior is maintained in the face of substantial social punishment.

maladaptive response   An instrumentally conditioned response for which the reinforcement is the escape or avoidance of stimulation that is not truly harmful to the organism. A response made at great sacrifice of energy, perhaps even harmful to the organism, for a reinforcement of dubious or nonexistent actual value. A two-factor word.

massed practice   Voluntarily repeating a response in the presumed or controlled absence of reinforcement in order to achieve extinction. It differs from nonreinforcement in that the client is instructed to produce the response repeatedly during massed practice, but during nonreinforcement the response is simply allowed to occur at whatever frequency prevails. A two-factor technique.

modify   To change the frequency at which a response occurs, either by increasing it, as with reinforcement, or by decreasing it, as with extinction. To change the *form* of a response by changing the frequency of one or more of its components.

negative emotion   Also *negative emotional response*. An all-inclusive term used when one does not wish to distinguish between fear, anxiety, guilt, or stress. A two-factor term.

negative reinforcement   The momentary withdrawal of an ongoing stimulus contingent on the occurrence of a particular response so as to make that response occur more often. Both before-the-fact and after-the-fact definitions are used (See positive reinforcement).

negative stimulus   A stimulus that an experimenter has reason to believe the subject will avoid. A punisher. An unpleasant, annoying, threatening, noxious, or aversive stimulus. If a negative stimulus were made contingent on a response in an instrumental conditioning procedure, one would expect the response to occur less often in the future. If a negative stimulus were made contingent on a neutral stimulus in a classical conditioning procedure, one would expect the response that originally occurred in the presence of the negative stimulus to occur more often in the presence of the originally neutral stimulus. A two-factor word.

neutral stimulus   A stimulus that an experimenter has reason to believe the subject will neither approach nor avoid. A stimulus that is neither pleasant nor unpleasant. A two-factor word.

noncontingent   Does not follow as a consequence of. Usually used to describe stimuli that might otherwise be mistakingly thought of as contingent. Consequently, *noncontingent* often refers to stimuli that occur at the same general time (see concomitant behavior) or immediately before or after a response but which were not a consequence of the response.

nonreinforcement   In operant conditioning, the procedure of discontinuing the response-contingent presentation of a stimulus that has resulted in acquisition, so that extinction will take place. The term *nonreinforcement* is also, but more rarely, used to describe the procedure in classical conditioning of presenting the conditioned stimulus in the absence of the unconditioned stimulus. The more common term for this procedure is *deconditioning*. See also massed practice.

observable   Capable of measurement with reliability. Note that the use of instruments to assist an observer introduces a certain degree of inference. As a result, events may be *more or less observable* as well as *observable and nonobservable.*

operant conditioning   Called instrumental conditioning by two-factor learning theorists. Any of a variety of procedures in which the experimenter or clinician arranges for a stimulus to occur consistently following the occurrence of a response. If the stimulus is a reinforcer, the response it follows would be expected to occur more often, but if the stimulus is a punisher, the response it follows would be expected to occur less often. This process is often theorized to be the way in which voluntary, skeletal muscle, or central nervous system behaviors are learned. For example, we work at our jobs because that activity is consistently followed by the agreeable consequence of receiving money. The frequency with which we go swimming decreases at the end of the summer as the water temperature falls, and the consequences of plunging in get more and more unpleasant.

operant response See "response."

positive emotion Also "positive emotional response." An all-inclusive term used when one does not wish to distinguish between relaxation, a feeling of well-being, satisfaction, contentment, or any other pleasant state. A two-factor term.

positive reinforcement Positive reinforcement may be defined before the fact as the repeated presentation of a positive stimulus contingent on the occurrence of a certain response. It may also be defined after the fact as an increase in the frequency at which a response occurs following the repeated presentation of a stimulus contingent on the occurrence of that response. Before-the-fact definitions characterize two-factor approaches, and after-the-fact definitions characterize operant conditioning approaches; there are some exceptions, however.

positive stimulus A stimulus that an experimenter has reason to believe the subject will approach. A reinforcer. A pleasant or satisfying stimulus. If a positive stimulus were made contingent on a response in an instrumental conditioning procedure, one would expect the response to occur more often in the future. If a positive stimulus were made contingent on a neutral stimulus in a classical conditioning procedure, one would expect the response that originally occurred in the presence of the positive stimulus to occur more often in the presence of the originally neutral stimulus. A two-factor term.

primary reinforcement Reinforcement the effectiveness of which does not depend on learning. Food and water are the best examples.

program A set of step-by-step procedures determined in advance for modifying behavior. The program determines what response or responses will be dealt with at different times; whether those responses will be reinforced, extinguished, or punished; the type, amount, and duration of the stimuli; the schedule of presentation; and any other details necessary to achieve conditioning. A program is composed of steps which progress in a specified sequence from a given starting point to a predetermined goal (see criterion). Some steps may be optional (see branching steps). An operant term.

punishment Punishment may be defined before the fact as the repeated presentation of a negative stimulus contingent on the occurrence of a certain response. It may be defined after the fact as a decrease in the frequency at which a response occurs following the repeated presentation of a stimulus contingent on the occurrence of that response. There is frequently a spontaneous recovery of the response after the punishing stimulation is discontinued.

reactive inhibition A temporary, unlearned reduction in the strength of a response caused by its repeated performance. As originally postulated by Hull, reactive inhibition was related to muscle fatigue, but the concept has also been applied to purely neurological or endocrine functions. A two-factor theoretical concept.

reinforcement In the operant position, any procedure in which a stimulus consistently follows a response and results in an increased frequency of that response's occurrence. In the two-factor position, either of two procedures: (1) presenting a positive stimulus contingent on a response, or (2) withdrawing a negative stimulus contingent on a response. In the operant position, the nature of the stimulus doesn't matter, but the outcome of the procedure does. In the two-factor position, the outcome of the procedure doesn't matter, but the nature of the stimulus does.

respondent conditioning See "classical conditioning."

response The basic units of behavior. What molecules are to the chemist, organisms to the zoologist, tissues to the histologist, stars to the astronomer, responses are to the behaviorist. For the operant conditioners (at least those who attended the Conference), all behavior can be divided up into responses, so that any organismic event is a response. The two-factor theorists, however (at least the one who attended this Conference) prefer to exclude certain organismic events from the category of responses. Organismic events caused by fatigue, drugs, or other physiological states, changes resulting from maturation or species-specific behavior (instinct) would be considered behavior but not responses. For the two-factor theorist, a response has to have been *learned* to be considered a response. Although the operant conditioners consider all behavior as made up of responses, they do not consider all responses as operants. In order to be an operant, a response must be capable of modification through operant procedures.

schedules (of reinforcement) The schedule of reinforcement refers to the amount of responding required to achieve reinforcement, as determined by an experimenter or clinician. The amount of responding may vary by number (i.e., reinforcing every response or every fourth response) or by the amount of time spent responding (i.e., reinforcing the first response after five minutes). The amount of responding required for reinforcement may also be programmed to vary in a manner unpredictable to the client.

shaping A technique for obtaining responses that are not originally in the subject's or client's repertoire. First, the desired response is specified. Then, responses which resemble that response, even remotely, are reinforced. Once the frequency of these responses has been increased, the criterion is changed so that in order to gain reinforcement, the subject must emit a response even more like the desired one. At this point, the technique is a special form of differential reinforcement. The criterion for reinforcement is continuously shifted in the direction of the desired response until that response is emitted, reinforced, and acquired. An operant word.

social reinforcement   In clinical or experimental descriptions, the use of approval or signs of friendship ("good," "right," "uh-huh," "mm-hmm," smiling, or nodding) as opposed to reinforcement that does not come from another person in a social interaction.

stimulus   Any event in an organism's environment to which the organism can respond. These events may occur within the organism (e.g., hunger pains) or outside. Stimuli are not limited to the sudden occurrence of something that was not occurring before, such as turning on a red light; they may also be the sudden nonoccurrence of something that was occurring before, such as turning *off* a red light (see negative reinforcement); nor need they be sudden—slow events, even the passage of time itself, can be stimuli.

stimulus generalization   The process by which a response which is instrumentally or classically conditioned to occur in the presence of a certain stimulus will also occur in the presence of similar stimuli, which were not presented during conditioning, to the degree that they are similar to the original stimulus.

stimulus situation   All of the stimuli, or at least all of the pertinent stimuli, impinging on an organism at any given moment.

suppression   Any of a number of effects, not dependent on learning, which result in a temporary decrease in the frequency with which a response occurs.

symptom substitution   The idea that the removal of one symptom will only result in the client's substituting another one for it. The concept rests on the assumption that there is some internal problem for which the symptom is only an outward manifestation. For most behaviorists, however, the symptoms (the behavior) *are* the problem.

target response   ' A response singled out by an experimenter or clinician, or specified in a program, as one that will receive some predetermined consequence, such as punishment or reinforcement. An operant word.

two-factor learning theory   The theory that learning takes place through both classical and instrumental conditioning. Some theorists postulate a relationship between the two theoretical types of learning: classical conditioning is thought to be responsible for the acquisition of the motivations for instrumental acts. For example,

157

money has no value to an infant, but by repeated association (classical conditioning) with the things it buys, it acquires a positive value. Once that positive value is acquired, the giving of money contingent on the performance of instrumental acts (instrumental conditioning) will increase the frequency with which those acts occur.

unconditioned stimulus In classical conditioning, the stimulus that reflexively upon presentation of the unconditioned stimulus.

unconditioned response In classical conditioning, the response made will regularly and reliably result in the occurrence of the unconditioned response. Unconditioned stimuli may be either positive (food) or negative (electric shock). Each unconditioned stimulus always elicits the same unconditioned response, e.g., food always results in salivation, electric shock always results in the withdrawal of the shocked part.

The following publications are sponsored
by the Speech Foundation of America.

STUTTERING AND ITS TREATMENT *(Publication No. 1)*

Published in the interest of making available to speech therapists and other interested parties, the agreements reached by a group of leading authorities concerning the methods to be used in helping to relieve the adult stutterer of his problem—a 48-page booklet.

STUTTERING WORDS *(Publication No. 2)*

An authoritative glossary of the meanings of the words and terms used or associated with the field of stuttering and in connection with its treatment. Definitions written with the cooperation of several speech pathologists—a 44-page booklet.

STUTTERING: ITS PREVENTION *(Publication No. 3)*

Written by a group of eminent speech pathologists for parents who do not want their children to stutter and especially for those parents of very young children who think they have reason to be concerned about their child's speech—a 64-page booklet.

TREATMENT OF THE YOUNG STUTTERER
IN THE SCHOOL *(Publication No. 4)*

An outline of the problems encountered by the speech therapist working with stutterers in the elementary school. Answering questions asked by public school therapists as to how to work in therapy with the young stutterer—a 64-page booklet.

STUTTERING: TRAINING THE THERAPIST
(Publication No. 5)

An outline of a suggested course of study to be used in training speech therapy students how to cope with the baffling problems they encounter in working with the stutterer—a 96-page booklet.

STUTTERING: SUCCESSES AND FAILURES IN THERAPY
(Publication No. 6)

Case histories of successes and failures in the treatment of stuttering by nine leading speech pathologists describing the procedures used in each case and the results attained—with the interesting comments from a conference reviewing these case histories—a 148 page book.

CONDITIONING IN STUTTERING THERAPY
(Publication No. 7)

Exploring the conditioning behavior modification approach to the treatment of stuttering with articles by authorities advocating its use and some criticism of its desirability together with a summary of conference discussions on the subject and a glossary of conditioning terms.

Publications No. 1 through No. 5—25c each
Publications No. 6 and 7—$1.00 each

Available from the Speech Foundation of America,
152 Lombardy Road, Memphis, Tennessee 38111